Grammar
PRACTICE BOOK

Macmillan
McGraw-Hill

The McGraw·Hill Companies

 **Macmillan
McGraw-Hill**

Published by Macmillan/McGraw-Hill, of McGraw-Hill Education, a division of The McGraw-Hill Companies, Inc.,
Two Penn Plaza, New York, New York 10121.

Printed in the United States of America

7 8 9 10 079 09 08 07

Contents

Unit 2 • Take A Stand

Unit 3 • Making A Difference

Unit 4 • Viewpoints

Unit 5 • Relationships

Unit 6 • Discovery

Name_____

- A **sentence** is a group of words that express a complete thought.
- A **sentence fragment** is a group of words that does not express a complete thought.
- A **statement** is a sentence that tells something.
- A **question** is a sentence that asks something.
- All sentences begin with a capital letter and end with a period or question mark.

Write *sentence, question,* or *fragment* for each group of words. Write each group of words as a sentence with the correct punctuation.

1. the cat feeds her kittens

_____

2. is very hungry today

_____

3. his lunch bag is missing

_____

4. did you bring your lunch

_____

5. he ate a tuna fish sandwich

_____

6. because he likes tuna fish

_____

7. what else do you think he likes

_____

8. the cat ate a worm

_____

© Macmillan/McGraw-Hill

At Home: Have your child write sentences and questions about mysteries.

The Mystery of the Missing Lunch

Grade 4/Unit 1

1

Name_____

> - A **statement** is a sentence that tells something. It ends with a period. **.**
> - A **question** is a sentence that asks something. It ends with a question mark. **?**
> - A **command** tells or asks someone to do something. It ends with a period. **.**
> - An **exclamation** shows strong feeling. It ends with an exclamation mark. **!**

Write each sentence with the correct punctuation.

1. Are you sure you brought your lunch

_____

2. Maybe Jack took it

_____

3. Class, stay in your seats

_____

4. Don't you dare say I stole it

_____

_____

5. Have you seen a stray cat in the building

_____

6. Cats like eating fish

_____

7. I can't believe the cat took the sandwich

_____

_____

8. Do you think we should feed the cat each day

_____

At Home: Have your child think of his or her favorite animal and write a statement, a question, a command, and an exclamation about it.

Name_____

> - Every **sentence** begins with a capital letter.
> - A **question** ends with a question mark.
> - A **statement** or a **command** ends with a period.
> - An **exclamation** ends with an exclamation mark.

Read each sentence. Rewrite it with the correct capital letters and punctuation.

1. I'm starving

_____

2. are you allergic to cats

_____

3. mother cats protect their kittens

_____

4. let me know if you find out who did it

_____

5. he was glad the mystery was solved

_____

6. don't jump to conclusions

_____

_____

7. who brought the peanut butter and jelly

_____

8. wow, this is a great cat

_____

_____

© Macmillan/McGraw-Hill

At Home: Read different kinds of sentences aloud. Ask your child how to punctuate each sentence.

The Mystery of the Missing Lunch

3

Grade 4/Unit 1

Name_____

- A **sentence** is a group of words that express a complete thought.
- A **sentence fragment** is a group of words that does not express a complete thought.
- A **statement** is a sentence that tells something.
- A **question** is a sentence that asks something.
- All sentences begin with a capital letter and end with a period or question mark.

Read the passage. Think about what type of sentence each one is. Then rewrite the passage using the correct punctuation.

when our cat had her kitten, we did not know what we would do a grown-up cat can be left by itself a baby kitten needs someone to watch her who could we get to care for her all day long I go to school all day mom and Dad go to work all day could Grandpa take the kitten grandpa said he could now the kitten lives with Grandpa We visit them every weekend It's wonderful

_____

_____

_____

_____

_____

_____

_____

At Home: Watch TV with your child. Repeat a line a character speaks and determine how the line would be punctuated in writing.

Name_____

A. Decide if each sentence is a *statement*, a *question*, a *command*, or an *exclamation*. Write what type of sentence each is.

1. His favorite sandwich is salami.

   _____

2. Can you lend me a dollar?

   _____

3. Don't forget your lunch.

   _____

4. The kittens are hiding.

   _____

5. What a funny story!

   _____

6. That stain looks like mustard.

   _____

B. Write each sentence with the correct punctuation.

7. I thought Jack took my lunch

   _____

8. Did you ever make a mistake like that

   _____

9. Cats are my favorite pets

   _____

10. I don't have any money

    _____

11. Wow, I can't believe the cat ate my lunch

    _____

12. Bring the kittens to my office

    _____

Name_____

- A **statement** is a sentence that tells something. It ends with a period. **.**
- A **question** is a sentence that asks something. It ends with a question mark. **?**
- A **command** tells or asks someone to do something. It ends with a period. **.**
- An **exclamation** shows strong feeling. It ends with an exclamation mark. **!**

Write each sentence with the correct capital letters and punctuation.

1. where is the mother cat

_____

2. give me the sandwich, please

_____

3. hey, you solved the mystery

_____

4. I like peanut butter and jelly

_____

5. what's going on here

_____

6. My cat stole one of my socks

_____

_____

7. Where do you think I found it

_____

8. It was in my cat's bed

_____

_____

© Macmillan/McGraw-Hill

Name_____

- The **subject** of a sentence is the person, place, or thing the sentence tells about.
- The **complete** subject includes all the words in the subject.
- The **simple** subject is usually a **noun** or a pronoun—the main word or words in the complete subject.
- A **compound** subject has two or more nouns that make up the subject.

Turn these sentence fragments into complete sentences by adding a subject. Write each complete sentence on the line.

1. are very dry.

_____

2. live for 200 years!

_____

3. come out at night.

_____

4. come out during the day.

_____

5. are reading about deserts.

_____

6. caught the lizard.

_____

7. are eaten by coyotes.

_____

8. is dangerous.

_____

Name_____

> - The **predicate** tells what the subject does or did.
> - The **complete** predicate includes all the words in the predicate.
> - The **simple** predicate is the verb—the action word or words or linking verb in the complete predicate.
> - A **compound predicate** has two or more verbs.

Turn these fragments into complete sentences by adding a predicate. Write each complete sentence on the line.

1. Plants in the deserts

_____

2. Most spiders

_____

3. Dangerous scorpions

_____

4. A quick coyote

_____

5. Hungry lizards

_____

6. The spines of a cactus

_____

7. On their field trip, the students

_____

8. Animals that come out at night

_____

At Home: Together, read sentences from books, magazines, or newspapers. Help your child identify the predicate of each.

- The subject of a sentence tells whom or what the sentence is about.
- The predicate of a sentence tells what the subject does or is.
- You can sometimes correct a sentence fragment by adding a subject or a predicate.

Read these sentence fragments and turn them into complete sentences by adding a subject or predicate.

1. This desert

_____

2. Walked a long way

_____

3. Heard the wind in the distance

_____

4. The coyote on the hill

_____

5. Was very thirsty

_____

6. A scorpion

_____

7. The kids and their parents

_____

8. Looked for water

_____

At Home: With your child, write sentence fragments on a piece of paper. Exchange papers and add a subject or predicate to each fragment.

A Walk in the Desert • **Grade 4/Unit 1**   **9**

Name_____

- A complete sentence contains both a subject and a predicate.
- You can sometimes correct a sentence fragment by adding a subject or a predicate.

Rewrite the advertisement. Correct the sentence fragments, punctuation, and capitalization.

A brand new video "Desert Adventure" must find water in the desert. Scorpions and coyotes will be after you. is there water behind the mesquite trees. Watch out for A rattlesnake can you escape them all? Enjoy the excitement of This game

_____

_____

_____

_____

_____

_____

At Home: Read your child's rewrite of the above advertisement. Ask your child which sentences have simple or compound subjects or predicates.

Name_____

A. Draw a line separating the complete subject from the complete predicate in each sentence. Then write the simple subject and the simple predicate on the line.

example: A cactus | stores water. cactus, stores

1. Desert weather is very dry. _____

2. Wood rats in the desert build huge nests. _____

3. The skin of a lizard seals water inside it. _____

4. The mother carried her babies. _____

5. Deserts get cooler at night. _____

B. Write the subject and predicate in each sentence below.

6. John packed some snacks and drank lots of water.

   Simple Subject: _____

   Compound Predicate: _____

7. Roadrunners and scorpions live in the desert.

   Compound Subject: _____

   Simple Predicate: _____

8. The spider spun a web and caught the insect.

   Simple Subject: _____

   Compound Predicate: _____

9. Rabbits and coyotes run very fast.

   Compound Subject: _____

   Simple Predicate: _____

10. The darkness and cool air refresh me at night.

    Compound Subject: _____

    Simple Predicate: _____

Name_____

- The subject is the person, place, or thing a sentence tells about.
- The simple subject is a noun—the main word or words in the complete subject.
- The predicate tells what the subject does or did.
- The simple predicate is the verb—the action word or words in the complete predicate.

Look at the picture below. Add a subject or a predicate to each sentence describing the picture.

1. _____ gives some shade.

2. Prickly cacti _____

3. The _____ was ready to strike.

4. A bird called a roadrunner _____

5. _____ are in the desert.

Name _____

> • A simple sentence contains one subject and one predicate. It contains one complete thought.
> • Two simple sentences may be joined to form a compound sentence, which contains two subjects and two predicates. It contains two complete thoughts.
> • A conjunction is used to combine the two sentences. *And, but*, and *or* are conjunctions.

Add a comma followed by *and, but,* or *or* to combine each pair of simple sentences into one compound sentence.

1. Elks have come back to the park. Wolves have returned, too.

_____

_____

2. I would like to visit the park often. I live far too away.

_____

_____

3. Visitors like the flowers in the park. They should not pick them.

_____

_____

4. You can look at the geysers in the park. You can enjoy the waterfalls instead.

_____

_____

5. I love Yellowstone Park. My brother prefers the beach.

_____

_____

6. My aunt came with me to the park. She said it was beautiful.

_____

At Home: Talk about the kind of park your child would like to see.

Name _____

> - A **compound subject** contains two or more simple subjects
>   that have the same predicate.
>   My **mother** *and* my **sister** looked at the map.
> - A **compound predicate** contains two or more simple
>   predicates that have the same subject.
>   The leaves **fall** *and* **cover** the ground.
> - You can join two sentences that have two subjects or two
>   predicates with the word *and* or *or*.

Combine each pair of sentences to form one sentence.

1. Some logs are 100 feet long. They are very colorful.

_____

2. Rainwater boils. It turns to steam.

_____

3. Old Faithful is a geyser. So is the Giantess.

_____

4. Water shoots up in geysers. It bubbles in ponds.

_____

5. The elks made a long journey. The elks traveled 2,500 miles.

_____

6. Elks live in the park. Bears live in the park.

_____

7. Forest fires burn in the park. They affect millions of acres.

_____

8. My dad likes camping. So does my sister.

_____

 At Home: Talk about national parks or another subject. As
you talk, ask your child to create compound sentences.

Name_____

> • Use a comma before *and, but*, or *or* when you join two
>   sentences to form a compound sentence.
> • Do not use a comma before *and* when you combine two
>   subjects or two predicates.

**Use *and*, *or*, or *but* to combine two sentences into a compound
sentence. Or, use *and* or *or* to combine subjects or predicates.**

1. My family loves camping. I prefer reading indoors.

_____

2. A volcano steams. A volcano erupts.

_____

3. Mom likes to hike. I come with her.

_____

4. A moose might walk by. A wolf might walk by.

_____

5. Fire burned some of the park. Other parts were untouched.

_____

6. Karen went hiking. I'm going with her next time.

_____

7. The Lower Falls are well known. Others don't even have a name.

_____

_____

8. Serena is camping. Maria is camping.

_____

At Home: With your child, look for examples of compound
sentences. Ask your child to tell you what simple sentences
were combined.

Our National Parks • **Grade 4/Unit 1** 15

- You can combine two sentences by using *and*, *but*, or *or*.
- You can combine two sentences by joining two subjects or two predicates with *and* or *or*.

Read the passage. Think about how two sentences are joined. Then rewrite the passage using the correct punctuation.

I enjoyed reading about Yellowstone National Park and I learned a lot from the book. at Yellowstone, you can see wolves or you might notice elks. I have been camping many times but I never saw those animals. the book describes geysers and forests. my family has never been to Yellowstone but this book made me want to go. maybe my family will visit Yellowstone someday!

_____

_____

_____

_____

_____

 At Home: Write or copy a brief passage making mistakes in punctuation and capitalization. Have your child proofread it.

A. Combine each pair of simple sentences with *and*, *but*, or *or*.

1. The volcano erupts. Molten rock flows out.

_____

2. Yellowstone is a great place. I like other parks too.

_____

3. We'll go camping together. We might go to the beach.

_____

4. Kyle forgot to pack a tootbrush. Susan forgot to bring soap.

_____

_____

5. Mom likes to hike. Dad likes to fish.

_____

B. Combine each pair of sentences by joining their subjects or predicates with *and*.

6. Ava cooked hot dogs. Trey cooked hot dogs.

_____

7. Koala bears live in Australia. Kangaroos live in Australia.

_____

8. Fish swim in the lake. Fish find food in the lake.

_____

9. Dad packed the knapsack. He put it over his shoulder.

_____

10. Sarah gathered wood for the fire. James gathered wood for the fire.

_____

Name_____

- A **compound sentence** contains two sentences joined by *and, but,* or *or.*
- A **compound subject** contains two or more simple subjects that have the same predicate.
- A **compound predicate** contains two or more simple predicates that have the same subject.

Write a short passage about the picture. Use two compound sentences and several simple sentences in your passage.

_____

_____

_____

_____

_____

Name_____

- A conjunction joins words, groups of words, or sentences.
- *And*, *but*, or *or* combine sentences.
- Some conjunctions tell *where, when*, *why*, *how*, or *under what condition*.

where	when	why	how	although
as	before	because	as if	if
as soon as	after	since	as though	unless

Combine each pair of sentences using the given conjunction.

1. The night became very dark. A cloud hid the moon. (when)

_____

2. Gracie reads books about the moon. She comes home. (as soon as)

_____

3. People weigh less on the moon. Gravity is weaker there. (because)

_____

4. I've studied stars and planets. I was eight years old. (since)

_____

5. I always put on my spacesuit. I leave the ship. (before)

_____

6. You can't breathe on the moon. You bring an oxygen tank. (unless)

_____

7. Earth looks like a big blue marble. You see it from outer space. (if)

_____

8. Astronauts visited the moon. The moon is over 250,000 miles away. (although)

_____

© Macmillan/McGraw-Hill

At Home: With your child, read the sentences above. Ask your child if the conjuctions could be used in a different place in the sentence.

Name_____

> • A sentence that contains two related ideas joined by a conjunction other than *and*, *but*, or *or* is called a **complex sentence**.

To form a complex sentence, combine these ideas using the given conjunction. Be sure that the new sentence makes sense.

1. The astronaut eats his meal. He floats around in the rocket. (as)

_____

_____

2. Light leaves a star. It takes thousands of years to reach Earth. (after)

_____

_____

3. Eat some freeze-dried snacks. You work at the computer. (while)

_____

_____

4. He goes to the library. He reads books about space. (where)

_____

5. Mom doesn't want me to come along. It is dangerous. (since)

_____

6. Fasten your seatbelts. The ship takes off. (before)

_____

7. He brought a chunk of moon rock. He came home for the holidays. (when)

_____

_____

8. They watched. The rocket blasted off into space. (as)

_____

© Macmillan/McGraw-Hill

At Home: Work with your child to write complex sentences using each of these conjunctions: *where*, *before*, and *because*.

Name_____

> - A complex sentence features an independent clause and one or more dependent clauses.
> - It does not always need a comma.

Rewrite this paragraph using complex sentences.

I was a little girl I have wanted to be an astronaut. I would read books about space. I felt like getting right into a rocket ship. I want to see the Red Planet, Mars, most of all. It represents action and energy. Red is my favorite color. I want to try to make my dream come true I grow up. I plan to go to college and I can major in astronomy. I can train in a space program.

_____
_____
_____
_____
_____
_____
_____
_____

© Macmillan/McGraw-Hill

At Home: Help your child add more complex sentences to this paragraph. Watch for run-ons.

Name_____

- Remember that some conjuctions tell *where*, *when*, *why*, *how*, or *under what condition*.

Rewrite the letter below. Fix any spelling, punctuation, and grammar mistakes.

678 Saturn Road
Baltimore, MD 21204
July 11, 2007

Mr. and Mrs. Rhodes
39 Sunshine Drive
Baltimore, MD 21286

Dear Mr. and Mrs. Rhodes,

I would like to be an astronaut. Because it would be exciting. You were the first people to travel to Mars. I bet you know a lot about space travel. I would like to learn more about outer space? I want to travel to mars someday. I also plan to visit Jupiter and Venus. Do you know which schools I could go to!

Sincerely,
Diana Smith

_____

_____

_____

_____

_____

_____

At Home: Write a short, silly paragraph with mistakes in complex sentences. Ask your child to point out the errors.

Name _____

Choose the best conjunction to combine each pair of sentences.

1. It was the year 1969 _____ the first person walked on the moon.

 a until
 b as if
 c when
 d since

2. A month will pass _____ we see a full moon again.

 e before
 f unless
 g as
 h as soon as

3. You need to wear a space suit _____ the temperatures are extreme.

 a although
 b because
 c after
 d why

4. He jumped high off the ground _____ his body were weightless.

 e how
 f before
 g as if
 h until

5. I would not move to the moon _____ it is a beautiful place.

 a if
 b after
 c as though
 d although

Name_____

A sentence that contains two related ideas joined by a conjunction other than *and*, *but*, or *or* is called a **complex sentence**.

where	when	why	how	although
as	before	because	as if	if
as soon as	after	since	as though	unless

Combine each pair of sentences to form a complex sentence. Choose conjunctions from the box above to connect them. Be sure that the new sentence makes sense.

1. I want to be an astronaut. Astronauts explore outer space.

_____

_____

2. Sunlight travels 93 million miles. It reaches Earth.

_____

_____

3. Pluto was discovered. Scientists discovered the other planets.

_____

_____

4. Bring a spacesuit. You visit the moon.

_____

_____

5. We can't live on Pluto. It is too cold.

_____

_____

> - A **run-on sentence** joins together two or more sentences that should be written separately.
>
>   The boy found the raft the raft floated down the river.
>
> - You can correct a run-on sentence by separating two complete ideas into two sentences. Each sentence should have a subject and a verb.
>
>   The boy found the raft. The raft floated down the river.

Correct the run-on sentences by separating them into two sentences. Each sentence should have a subject and a verb.

1. I'm bored at Grandma's house she doesn't have a TV.

_____

2. We're going bird watching you can bring your friend along.

_____

3. The raft floated by he wondered where it came from.

_____

4. The animals are fascinating I will try drawing them.

_____

5. I played with the otters they let me feed them.

_____

6. Grandma found a pearl inside the clam she kept it for years.

_____

7. He draws a picture on the raft he draws well.

_____

8. Grandma loves the river she uses the raft to float on it.

_____

At Home: Take turns writing run-on sentences and correcting them.

The Raft • **Grade 4/Unit 1** **25**

- You can correct a **run-on sentence** by rewriting it as a compound or a complex sentence.

Correct these run-on sentences by rewriting them as compound or complex sentences. Be sure that the new sentence makes sense.

1. I thought the visit would be boring I had a fun time.

_____

2. I woke up the birds started chirping.

_____

3. She looked at the drawings wondered who drew them.

_____

_____

4. He's never been on a boat he's afraid he'll get seasick.

_____

_____

5. Grandma is an artist is carving a bear.

_____

6. You can go on the raft you must wear a life jacket.

_____

_____

7. The fawn was trapped I set her free.

_____

8. We have to be careful the water is deep.

_____

At Home: With your child, write a few run-on sentences. Practice rewriting them as compound or complex sentences.

Name_____

- You can correct a run-on sentence by separating two complete ideas into two sentences. Make sure each sentence starts with a capital letter and ends with a period.
- You can correct a run-on sentence by rewriting it as a compound or complex sentence. Be sure to use a comma before *and*, *but*, or *or*.

Correct the following run-on sentences. Separate the parts into two sentences, or join the parts into one compound or complex sentence.

1. The workroom is messy there are books, sketches, and fishing poles everywhere.

_____

_____

2. We want to camp out it is too cold outdoors.

_____

3. It is difficult to photograph the buck it gets frightened and runs away.

_____

_____

4. Hal likes his raft Hal fishes off it.

_____

5. I travel on the raft I push it along with a pole.

_____

6. The deer came right up to me it was not scared at all.

_____

At Home: With your child, read the fragments above and find other ways to correct them.

Name_____

- A run-on sentence joins together two or more sentences.
- You can correct a run-on sentence by separating two complete ideas into two sentences.
- You can correct a run-on sentence by rewriting it as a compound or complex sentence.

Rewrite the journal entry below, correcting any punctuation and grammar mistakes. Be sure to fix any run-on sentences.

April 10 2005

Mom, Dad, Dave, and I went rafting on Foamy river today we had so much fun! We were worried about the water being cold it is only April. We brought extra sweaters. Of course, we also brought our lifejackets? Dave and I wanted to steer the raft we were too little. The current was very strong. The raft went up and down we got splashed a few times. We passed the woods my brother saw a deer. At the end of the day we were tired we want to go again soon.

_____

_____

_____

_____

_____

_____

_____

At Home: With your child, take turns writing passages with grammar and punctuation mistakes. Exchange passages and correct them.

Name_____

A. Correct these run-on sentences by separating them into two sentences.

1. Have you ever been on a raft it's lots of fun.

_____

2. My grandfather is a painter he paints animals.

_____

3. I woke up a huge buck was standing there.

_____

4. Beavers are so funny-looking have you ever seen one?

_____

5. I drew the fawn I showed it to Grandma.

_____

B. Rewrite the following run-on sentences as compound or complex sentences. Be sure that the new sentences make sense.

6. You should bring your life jacket the water is deep.

_____

_____

7. He had to walk quietly the deer would run away.

_____

8. I invited Bob to visit he likes the outdoors.

_____

9. Kerry watched sadly the otters swam away.

_____

10. I was sad to leave the river I was glad to be going home.

_____

_____

Name_____

- A **run-on sentence** joins together two or more sentences that should be written separately.
- You can correct a run-on sentence by separating two complete ideas into two sentences.
- You can correct a run-on sentence by rewriting it as a compound or complex sentence.

Add capital letters, conjunctions, and punctuation marks to turn each group of words into one or two sentences that tell about the picture.

1. we love the lake so many animals live there

_____

2. it's hard to catch rabbits they run away so fast

_____

3. deer get frightened they see or hear you

_____

4. the raccoon's eyes are black he's wearing a mask

_____

5. most birds can fly some cannot

_____

Read each passage and look at the underlined parts. What kind of sentences are they? Circle your answers.

Ramon felt so frustrated. (1) Who could have stolen his lunch? "I need to tell you something," he said to Jack. (2) "Don't go anywhere."

1. A. Statement   **2. E.** Statement
   B. Question   **F.** Question
   C. Command   **G.** Command
   D. Exclamation   **H.** Exclamation

Some desert animals come out only at nighttime. (3) It is cooler then. The kangaroo rat is nocturnal. (4) Have you ever seen one?

3. A. Statement   **4. E.** Statement
   B. Question   **F.** Question
   C. Command   **G.** Command
   D. Exclamation   **H.** Exclamation

(5) What fun it is to go to the park! I've been to Yellowstone National Park three times. Carol has never been there. (6) Ask her to come along.

5. A. Statement   **6. E.** Statement
   B. Question   **F.** Question
   C. Command   **G.** Command
   D. Exclamation   **H.** Exclamation

Read each passage and look at the underlined sentences. Is there a mistake? If there is, how do you correct it? Circle your answers.

We all feel so much lighter on the moon. (7) <u>The force of gravity.</u> I can jump two feet into the air. (8) <u>It's easy. You should try it!</u>

7. A. Add a subject.
    B. Add a predicate.
    C. Join two sentences with *and.*
    D. No mistake.

8. E. Add a subject.
    F. Add a predicate.
    G. Join two sentences with *and.*
    H. No mistake.

I took the raft out on the lake. (9) <u>Came with me.</u> (10) <u>It was cold we didn't stay long.</u>

9. A. Add a subject.
    B. Add a predicate.
    C. Join two sentences with *and.*
    D. No mistake.

10. E. Add a subject.
    F. Add a predicate.
    G. Join two sentences with *and.*
    H. No mistake.

(11) <u>I love to sketch animals.</u> (12) <u>My grandfather an experienced painter.</u> I visit him and sketch the animals on his farm.

11. A. Add a subject.
    B. Add a predicate.
    C. Join two sentences with *and.*
    D. No mistake.

12. E. Add a subject.
    F. Add a predicate.
    G. Join two sentences with *and.*
    H. No mistake.

> - A **noun** names a person, place, or thing.
> - A **common noun** names any person, place, or thing.
>   Examples: teacher   city   dog
> - A **common noun** does not begin with a capital letter.
> - A **common noun** does *not* name a particular person, place,
>   or thing. These words are not common nouns: Mr. Smith,
>   Chicago, Spot.

Underline the common nouns in each sentence.

1. Baseball is my favorite sport.

2. The pitcher is named Jackie.

3. My father says the New York Yankees are a great team.

4. Listen to the noise of the crowd sitting in the bleachers.

5. Alissa said the umpire was wrong.

6. Alex and Daniel play baseball in the backyard.

7. My sister uses a wooden bat.

8. Don't throw the ball in the house!

9. The batter has two strikes.

10. John lost his mitt.

11. Your foot has to touch the base.

12. Let's keep track of the game.

13. That ball is a foul.

14. Did you bring your cleats?

At Home: Ask your child to write two sentences about the
story and underline the common nouns.

Mighty Jackie • **Grade 4/Unit 2**   33

Name_____

- A **proper noun** names a particular person, place, or thing.
  Examples: Ms. Brown   San Francisco   Atlantic Ocean.
- A **proper noun** begins with a capital letter.
- Some proper nouns contain more than one word. Each important word begins with a capital letter.
  Examples: Statue of Liberty   Boston Red Sox
- The name of a day, month, or holiday begins with a capital letter.

Read the list of nouns below. Decide whether each noun is common or proper and write it in the correct column. Capitalize the nouns in the Proper column.

independence day	summer	uniform	new york
hank aaron	stadium	ebbets field	july
home plate	jackie robinson	coach	world series
diamond	game	shortstop	ohio

COMMON

_____

_____

_____

_____

_____

_____

PROPER

_____

_____

_____

_____

_____

_____

At Home: Have your child list two common nouns and two proper nouns.

Name_____

- Some proper nouns contain more than one word. Each important word begins with a capital letter.
- The name of a day, month, or holiday begins with a capital letter.

Capitalize the proper nouns found in each sentence.

1. I like to play baseball with my brother matt and his friends.

_____

_____

2. Last saturday, we played all afternoon.

_____

3. I am also part of the dallas little league.

_____

4. My cousin karen is the best pitcher I know.

_____

5. We play ball together when I visit her in florida.

_____

6. I haven't seen her since thanksgiving.

_____

7. She has a baseball card with a picture of mickey mantle.

_____

_____

8. My uncle went to a game at yankee stadium.

_____

© Macmillan/McGraw-Hill

At Home: Ask your child to write two sentences about the story. Then have your child underline the proper nouns.

Mighty Jackie • **Grade 4/Unit 2** **35**

- Some proper nouns contain more than one word. Each important word begins with a capital letter.
- The name of a day, month, or holiday begins with a capital letter.

Rewrite the invitation below. Fix any spelling, punctuation, and grammar mistakes. Remember to capitalize each important word in a proper noun. Use a separate page if you need more space.

westfield little league invites you to attend

our 2005 most valuable player awards ceremony

at five o'clock on sunday, january 30

westfield town hall

501 central avenue, westfield, virginia

Please contact sally and jim smith at 555-1212 if you plan to attend.

We hope you will join us!

_____

_____

_____

_____

_____

_____

_____

At Home: Have your child write a line from the corrected invitation on an index card. Discuss why it should be capitalized.

Name_____

Find the two nouns in each sentence and write them on the lines.

1. Yogi Berra is a famous coach. _____ _____

2. My uniform is in the dryer. _____ _____

3. The ball landed in Lake Superior. _____

   _____

4. Dr. Zed talked to my mom. _____

5. This bat is made of aluminum. _____ _____

6. I pitched the ball to the batter. _____ _____

7. Stretch your legs while in your sweatpants. _____

   _____

8. Write down the score of the game. _____

   _____

Use the nouns in the box to complete each sentence in a way that makes sense. Don't forget to capitalize any proper nouns.

jill	dog	february	idaho
autograph		bleachers	mitt

9. We drove from Nebraska to _____.

10. My _____ plays catch with me.

11. I asked for the pitcher's _____.

12. I've been practicing since _____.

13. Ask _____ to play with us.

14. We sat in the _____.

15. Where is my _____?

Name_____

- A **common noun** names any person, place, or thing.
- A **proper noun** names a particular person, place, or thing.

Mechanics

- Begin each important word in a proper noun with a capital letter.
- Begin the name of a day, holiday, or month with a capital letter.

Read each sentence. Write the underlined noun correctly on the line.

1. Jackie struck out <u>lou gehrig</u>. _____

2. This historic event took place in <u>tennessee</u>. _____

3. The team played against the <u>chattanooga lookouts</u>.

   _____

4. Babe Ruth didn't want to play against a <u>girl</u>. _____

5. My teacher, <u>ms. potter</u>, told me about the game. _____

Name_____

- A **singular noun** names one person, place, or thing.
  Examples: teacher, city, dog.
- A **plural noun** names more than one person, place, or thing.
  Examples: teachers, cities, dogs.
- Add -*s* to form the plural of most singular nouns.

Decide whether each underlined word is a singular or plural noun. Then write *singular* or *plural* on the line.

1. There are no <u>jobs</u> here. _____

2. My family is leaving the <u>country</u>. _____

3. We're going to stay with my <u>grandparents</u> for now. _____

4. Papa sent us a <u>letter</u>. _____

5. He is meeting us at the bus <u>station</u>. _____

6. We're waiting to get our green <u>cards</u>. _____

7. This <u>trip</u> is taking forever! _____

8. It's been <u>weeks</u> since I've seen you. _____

9. The <u>pages</u> of my diary are filling up. _____

10. I miss the <u>park</u> I used to go to. _____

11. I had to sell my <u>bike</u>. _____

12. The <u>apartment</u> is crowded. _____

13. I kept my two <u>parrots</u>. _____

14. We bought some new <u>clothes</u>. _____

15. She received several <u>letters</u>. _____

At Home: Have your child think of three singular nouns and three plural nouns naming items he or she would bring on a journey.

My Diary from Here to There **39**
Grade 4/Unit 2

Name_____

- Add -s to form the plural of most singular nouns.
- Add -es to form the plural of singular nouns that end in s, sh, ch, or x.
- To form the plural of nouns ending in a consonant and y, change y to i and add -es.
- To form the plural of nouns ending in a vowel and y, add -s.

Write the correct plural form of each noun in parentheses.

1. We saw (foxs) _____ running across the prairie.

2. Many people from other (countrys) _____ have come to the United States.

3. (Massies) _____ of people traveled to the west in the 1800s.

4. Some travelers keep (diarys) _____.

5. Gather a few (branchs) _____ so we can build a fire.

6. She caught a rabbit that was hiding in the (bushs) _____.

7. I asked the neighbor's two (boyes) _____ to help me milk the cow.

8. Some people used the old trail, but a few found new (pathway) _____.

9. That chest has many (scratchs) _____.

10. Please feed the (babys) _____.

11. We need more (boxs) _____ than that!

12. I will write two more (pagies) _____ today.

My Diary from Here to There
Grade 4/Unit 2

 At Home: Write down ten singular nouns. Have your child write the plural form.

Name _____

> • A **comma** tells the reader to pause between the words that it separates.
> • Use commas to separate three or more words in a series.
>   Example: We enjoyed the mountains, the trees, and the clouds in the park.
> • Do not use a comma after the last word in a series.

Rewrite the sentences below by adding commas where they belong.

1. He fed milked and groomed the cows.

   _____

2. Go to the store and get flour eggs and sugar.

   _____

3. Mexico Ireland and China are three countries I have visited.

   _____

4. Bring wood nails and a hammer.

   _____

5. We have mules horses and pigs on our ranch.

   _____

6. This city feels dirty strange and lonely.

   _____

7. Mosquitoes spiders and ants annoyed us.

   _____

8. I brought my diary my pencil and an eraser.

   _____

9. My mother father and brother are coming along.

   _____

10. I miss the house my dog and our friends.

    _____

At Home: Write three sentences without commas. Then, have your child rewrite them correctly using commas.

Name_____

> • Add *-s* to form the plural of most singular nouns.
> • Add *-es* to form the plural of singular nouns that end in *s, sh, ch,* or *x.*
> • To form the plural of nouns ending in a consonant and *y,* change *y* to *i* and add *-es.*
> • To form the plural of nouns ending in a vowel and *y,* add *-s.*

Rewrite the radio advertisement below. Fix any spelling, punctuation, and grammar mistakes. Use a separate page if you need more space.

Looking for quick fixs for bath and shower time? Dr. Minty's Amazing 3-in-1 Gel is the answer! Use it to clean minor cuts and scratchs. It also works to soothe any itchs rashs or irritations of the skin. Lastly, it's a gentle cleansing alternative to harsh soaps and body washs. It's safe for adultes kids and even babys. The 3-in-1 Gel is available in boxs containing eight twelve or sixteen ounces. It's one of our best buyes—each box lasts for monthies!

_____

_____

_____

_____

_____

_____

_____

 At Home: Have your child write a line from the corrected advertisement.

Name_____

A. Read each sentence. Find the noun that is singular. Circle your answer.

1. Many families rode in covered wagons across the state.

   a. families   **b.** rode   **c.** wagons   **d.** state

2. My mother, sisters, and grandparents packed their clothes.

   a. mother   **b.** sisters   **c.** grandparents   **d.** clothes

3. I watched many sunsets over the beautiful lake.

   a. watched   **b.** sunsets   **c.** beautiful   **d.** lake

4. The hens, the old rooster, and the cows came with us.

   a. hens   **b.** rooster   **c.** cows   **d.** with

B. Read each sentence. Find the correct plural form for the nouns in parentheses. Circle your answer.

5. The blue (sky) over the prairies seem so vast and clear.

   a. skys   **b.** skyes   **c.** skies   **d.** skyies

6. We spent many (day) on our journey.

   a. days   **b.** dayes   **c.** daies   **d.** dayies

7. Be sure to avoid the swamps and (marsh).

   a. marshs   **b.** marshes   **c.** marshies   **d.** marshys

8. I've lived in several (city), but I prefer the country.

   a. citys   **b.** cityes   **c.** cities   **d.** cityies

Name_____

- Add -*s* to form the plural of most singular nouns.
- Add -*es* to form the plural of singular nouns that end in *s, sh, ch,* or *x*.
- To form the plural of nouns ending in a consonant and *y*, change *y* to *i* and add -*es*.
- To form the plural of nouns ending in a vowel and *y*, add -*s*.

Mechanics

- A **comma** tells the reader to pause between the words that it separates.
- Use commas to separate three or more words in a series.
- Do not use a comma after the last word in a series.

Correct each sentence below by changing the underlined singular noun to a plural, and by adding the missing commas. With a partner, take turns reading the corrected sentences aloud, pausing when you reach each comma.

1. We saved our <u>penny</u> nickels and dimes.

_____

2. They traveled on <u>bus</u> trains and planes.

_____

3. <u>Fox</u> dogs and squirrels were seen in the field.

_____

4. <u>Fly</u> ants and spiders lived near the swamp.

_____

5. I counted the <u>day</u> weeks and months.

_____

© Macmillan/McGraw-Hill

Name_____

- Some nouns have special plural forms.

calves	lice	children	feet	geese
gentlemen	leaves	potatoes	knives	halves
mice	wives	thieves	heroes	tomatoes
lives	men	women	oxen	teeth

Look in the above box for the plural form of each singular noun. Write it on the line provided.

1. man _____

2. child _____

3. woman _____

4. life _____

5. calf _____

6. thief _____

7. potato _____

8. goose _____

9. ox _____

10. wife _____

11. foot _____

12. hero _____

13. tooth _____

14. gentleman _____

15. knife _____

16. tomato _____

17. mouse _____

18. louse _____

19. leaf _____

20. half _____

© Macmillan/McGraw-Hill

At Home: Take turns with your child using the singular and plural nouns on this page in oral sentences.

- A few nouns have the same plural and singular form.
- To determine whether the noun is singular or plural, look at the rest of the sentence.

Read the sentences below. Then decide whether the underlined noun is *singular* or *plural*. Write your answer on the line.

1. There was not one <u>sheep</u> on Papa's farm. _____

2. A herd of <u>buffalo</u> trampled across the land. _____

3. <u>Moose</u> live in cold places, like Canada. _____

4. This species of <u>insect</u> only lives for two days. _____

5. I ate clams and <u>shrimp</u> at dinner. _____

6. Be quiet or you might scare that <u>deer</u> away. _____

7. We caught five <u>fish</u> today. _____

8. We saw a <u>moose</u> at the zoo. _____

9. He dipped each <u>shrimp</u> into the cocktail sauce. _____

10. <u>Sheep</u> produce wool for sweaters. _____

11. We raked the <u>leaves</u> today. _____

12. I am not afraid of the <u>mouse</u>. _____

13. She is getting her <u>teeth</u> cleaned. _____

14. Several <u>oxen</u> passed the ranch. _____

15. He wanted a baked <u>potato</u>. _____

At Home: Have your child write three sentences using the nouns above, stating if they are singular or plural.

© Macmillan/McGraw-Hill

Name_____

- Some nouns have special plural forms.
- A few nouns have the same singular and plural forms.

Read each sentence. Draw a line under the word in parentheses that is the correct plural form.

1. Chinese (factoryes, factories) produced lots of paper.

2. Wheelbarrows, invented in China, were compared to wooden (oxes, oxen).

3. Chinese inventors experimented with magnetism by placing iron (fish, fishes) in water.

4. The first kites floated through the air like (leafs, leaves).

5. I wonder who first realized it's a good idea to brush your (tooths, teeth)?

6. Magicians placed pieces of lodestone into the (bellys, bellies) of wooden turtles.

7. A member of the Chinese court invented a machine to predict (earthquakes, earthquaks).

8. I didn't know the Chinese had made (compassies, compasses).

9. I think of inventors as (heroes, heros).

10. What different (specieses, species) of animals come from China?

11. These inventions have changed many people's (lives, lifes).

12. (Tomatoes, Tomatos) come with the meal.

At Home: Have your child name the two nouns in the above sentences that have the same plural and singular forms.

- A few nouns have the same plural and singular form.
- To determine whether the noun is singular or plural, look at the rest of the sentence.

Rewrite the narrative below. Fix any spelling, punctuation, and grammar mistakes. Be sure to correct the eleven incorrectly formed plural nouns.

I want to be a chef who invents new, delicious dishs for people to enjoy! I decided this after visiting a new restaurant a few days ago. All of the mens, womans, and childs there watched the chef with great excitement. I watched him handle his long, sharp knifes carefully. Effortlessly, he diced potatos and tomatoeies into halfs and quarters. The shrimpses and fishies sizzled as he cooked them on the hot grill. When our excellent meal arrived, we really sank our toothes into it. That's when I decided cooking must be a fun way to be creative.

_____

_____

_____

_____

_____

_____

_____

_____

At Home: Have your child write a paragraph about traveling, using two irregular plural nouns.

Name_____

A. Write *yes* if the noun below has the same singular and plural forms. Write *no* if the noun does not have the same singular and plural forms.

1. ship _____

2. deer _____

3. calf _____

4. species _____

5. moose _____

6. ox _____

7. half _____

8. shrimp _____

B. Complete each sentence with the plural form of the singular noun in parentheses.

9. Two baby (calf) _____ were born last night.

10. Which of the inventors were (woman) _____?

11. It is easier for (child) _____ to learn a new language than it is for adults to learn one.

12. King Henry VIII had many (wife) _____.

13. There were a few (mouse) _____ under the stove in the kitchen.

14. The (thief) _____ were soon caught.

15. My (foot) _____ are so tired.

16. That dog has plenty of (louse) _____.

Name_____

- A few nouns have the same plural and singular form.
- To determine whether the noun is singular or plural, look at the rest of the sentence.

Mechanics

- A **proper noun** begins with a capital letter.
- The name of a day, month, or holiday begins with a capital letter.
- Capitalize family names if they refer to specific people.
- Capitalize titles of people before names.

Rewrite the sentences below. Fix any punctuation and grammar mistakes.

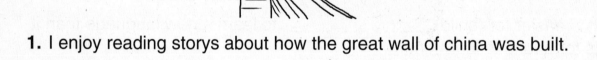

1. I enjoy reading storys about how the great wall of china was built.

_____

_____

2. I wonder how many mans and womens worked on it.

_____

3. My friend john wants to know how many foots long it is.

_____

4. Some people spent their whole lifes working on it.

_____

5. I will tell my childrens the story of the Great wall.

_____

Name_____

- A **possessive noun** is a noun that shows who or what owns or has something.
- A **singular possessive noun** is a singular noun that shows ownership.
- Form a singular possessive noun by adding an **apostrophe** (') and -s to a singular noun.

Write the possessive form of each underlined singular noun.

1. <u>Ben Franklin</u> almanacs are very funny to read. _____

2. The book is the <u>library</u>, so please return it. _____

3. People rang the <u>church</u> loud bells when there was a fire.

   _____

4. The <u>inventor</u> fame spread throughout the nation. _____

5. Have you seen <u>Mary</u> bifocals? _____

6. Ben Franklin was one of <u>America</u> best-known citizens.

   _____

7. This old <u>book</u> pages are torn. _____

8. My <u>doctor</u> advice is to exercise more. _____

9. The key was tied to the <u>kite</u> long string. _____

10. The <u>battery</u> power is running low. _____

11. The <u>lawyer</u> advice was quite helpful. _____

12. One <u>person</u> work is not enough today. _____

13. The <u>car</u> fender is dented. _____

14. I created the <u>office</u> design. _____

At Home: Have your child write four sentences using four of the singular possessive nouns above.

Name_____

- A **plural possessive noun** is a plural noun that shows ownership.
- To form the possessive of a plural that ends in *s*, add an apostrophe.
- To form the possessive of a plural noun that does not end in *s*, add an apostrophe and *-s*. A few nouns have the same plural and singular form.

Write the plural possessive form of each underlined noun.

1. Those <u>experiments</u> purpose was to teach us more about electricity.

   _____

2. For the first time, the post office delivered mail directly to <u>people</u>

   houses. _____

3. The mayor honored the <u>firefighters</u> heroism. _____

4. Electrical <u>charges</u> effects can be dangerous. _____

5. Ben Franklin won several <u>countries</u> respect. _____

6. The church <u>bells</u> ringing woke me. _____

7. Most <u>limes</u> skin is green, but one kind of lime is yellow.

   _____

8. The <u>children</u> book was very interesting. _____

9. That is the <u>workers</u> break room. _____

10. The <u>bulbs</u> shoots will sprout flowers. _____

11. Twelve <u>sinks</u> drains must be cleaned out. _____

12. The <u>insects</u> habits inspired my work. _____

13. <u>Airplanes</u> tires are fully inflated. _____

14. Those <u>objects</u> tags are missing. _____

At Home: Have your child write sentences using the possessive forms of these plural nouns: children, boys, girls, people.

Mechanics

Name_____

- Capitalize the first and last words and all important words in the titles of books and newspapers.
- Underline titles of books, newspapers, magazines, and TV series.
- Put quotation marks around the titles of short stories, articles, songs, poems, and book chapters.
- Remember to use apostrophes to form possessive nouns.

Rewrite each sentence, making sure the titles are written correctly.

1. One of Ben Franklin best-known books is titled poor Richard's almanac.

_____

_____

2. Lewis Latimer wrote a book called incandescent electric lighting in 1890.

_____

_____

3. I learned about Thomas Edison and Lewis Latimer from an article called great american inventors of the past.

_____

_____

4. The article was published in the magazine science for kids.

_____

_____

5. My friend is writing a short story titled the amazing mind of lewis latimer.

_____

_____

6. He hopes to get his story published in his local newspaper, the miami herald.

_____

_____

At Home: Write four familiar titles without capital letters, underlining, or quotation marks. Have your child rewrite the titles correctly.

How Ben Franklin Stole the Lightning • Grade 4/Unit 2   53

Name_____

- A **singular possessive noun** is a singular noun that shows ownership.
- A **plural possessive noun** is a plural noun that shows ownership.

Rewrite the book review below. Fix any spelling, punctuation, and grammar mistakes. Be sure to correct any mistakes in titles or possessive nouns.

I found Akimi Gibsons book, Lewis Howard Latimer: an inventive Mind, very interesting. Latimer, an African-American inventor, was born in the mid-1800s. He made drawings of other inventors creations, which were used to apply for patents. Then Latimers own ideas for inventions began to unfold. He helped improve the lavatories on trains and assisted with Alexander Graham Bells invention of the telephone. While working for the U. S. Electric Lighting Company, he found a way to protect light bulbses' filaments so they would not burn out quickly. This was a great improvement to Thomas Edisons' lightbulb. Gibsons biography of Latimer is an informative one.

_____

_____

_____

_____

_____

_____

_____

At Home: Have your child write two lines from the corrected book review.

© Macmillan/McGraw-Hill

Name_____

A Choose the correct singular possessive form to complete each sentence.

1. _____ invention changed the world.

   a. Edisons　　**b.** Edison'　　**c.** Edison's　　**d.** Edisons'

2. The _____ effect was devastating.

   a. fire'　　**b.** fire's　　**c.** fires'　　**d.** fires

3. The _____ temperature is warmer in some places.

   a. oceans　　**b.** oceans'　　**c.** ocean　　**d.** ocean's

4. The _____ laughter lasted a long time.

   a. king's　　**b.** kings　　**c.** kings'　　**d.** king'

B. Choose the correct plural possessive form to complete each sentence.

5. These _____ inventions were amazing!

   a. people　　**b.** peoples　　**c.** peoples'　　**d.** people's

6. African-American _____ right to take out patents was recognized after the Civil War.

   a. inventors　　**b.** inventor's　　**c.** inventors'　　**d.** inventor'

7. The _____ efforts led to a new creation.

   a. worker　　**b.** workers'　　**c.** workers　　**d.** worker's

8. The _____ amazement showed on their faces.

   a. childs'　　**b.** childrens'　　**c.** children's　　**d.** childrens

9. All of the _____ covers were torn.

   a. books　　**b.** books'　　**c.** book's　　**d.** book

10. The _____ purposes must be made clearer.

   a. experiments　　**b.** experiment's　　**c.** experiment'　　**d.** experiments'

Name_____

- A **singular possessive noun** is a singular noun that shows ownership.
- A **plural possessive noun** is a plural noun that shows ownership.

Mechanics

- Add an apostrophe and -*s* to a singular noun to make it possessive.
- Add an apostrophe to make most plural nouns possessive.
- Add an apostrophe and -*s* to form the possessive of plural nouns that do not end in *s*.

Read the sentences below. Make each underlined noun possessive.

1. What do you know about <u>electricity</u> effects? _____
2. <u>Engineers</u> jobs are very challenging. _____
3. That light <u>bulb</u> filament is burned out. _____
4. Find the <u>book</u> place on the shelf. _____
5. The <u>eyeglasses</u> lenses are scratched. _____
6. Those <u>people</u> help is very important. _____
7. The electrical <u>charges</u> power is strong. _____
8. Don't forget those <u>libraries</u> rules. _____
9. These <u>doctors</u> experiments worked well. _____
10. The <u>children</u> logs are detailed. _____

Name_____

- A **plural noun** names more than one person, place, or thing.
- Add -s to most nouns to form the plural. Do not use an apostrophe.
- To form the plural of most nouns that end in y, change the y to i and add -es.

Write the plural form of the noun in the parentheses on the line provided.

1. The two girls rode their (bike) _____ up the hill.

2. You're not allowed to bring (snake) _____ into the library.

3. (Library) _____ are good places to go to find information.

4. Some (book) _____ cannot be taken out of the library.

5. I bet the (person) _____ who work in libraries know a lot.

6. The library has a special section with books just for (child) _____.

7. I want to look up some (fact) _____ about snakes.

8. I am also checking out a book of short (story) _____.

9. A snake's (scale) _____ feel dry, not slimy.

10. I like to watch television shows about (animal) _____.

11. There are many (reptile) _____ to read about.

12. My favorite (stop) _____ are nature trails.

13. I found some great wildlife (magazine) _____.

14. We like the (museum) _____ in the city.

At Home: Have your child write five singular nouns. Then ask your child to write the plural form of each one.

Name_____

- A plural noun names more than one person, place, or thing.
- Add -s to most nouns to form the plural. Do not use an apostrophe.
- A **possessive noun** shows who or what owns or has something.
- Add an apostrophe (') and -s to a singular noun to make it possessive.

Write a plural noun or a possessive noun to complete each sentence. Use the singular nouns in the box to help you.

box	picture	snake	rattle	skin	prairie	book

1. She carried the noisy _____ from several snakes.

2. When he saw the rattlesnake, he was scared by the _____ sound.

3. I want to find some _____ about animals in the library.

4. This book has words but no _____.

5. This _____ photographs are very interesting.

6. Snakes shed their _____ when they grow.

7. Will you help me open those _____ to see what's inside?

8. A _____ bite may or may not contain poison.

9. Oh no, that _____ lid is moving!

10. Some types of snakes live in fields and _____.

At Home: Write two sentences, one with a plural noun and one with a possessive noun. Have your child identify which is which.

Name_____

> - Begin the greeting and closing of a letter with a capital letter.
> - Use a comma after the greeting and closing in a letter.
> - Use a comma between the names of a city and state.
> - Use a comma between the day and the year in a date.
> - Use the following abbreviations for people's titles: **Mr., Mrs., Ms., Dr.** (Doctor), **Jr.** (Junior), **Sr.** (Senior)
> - Use U.S. Postal service abbreviations for the state name.

Correctly rewrite the letter below.

506 Cedar Lane
albany, New York 10965
February 2 2004

Dear Doctor Mitchell,

Thank you so much for coming to speak to our class last month. We all really enjoyed your slide show about reptiles. Our teacher, Mister Nelson, taught a whole unit about reptiles that week.

Your friend
Bobby Hernandez

_____

_____

_____

_____

_____

_____

At Home: Have your child write a letter to a friend about something interesting that he or she learned.

Dear Mr. Winston

59

Grade 4/Unit 2

- A plural noun names more than one person, place, or thing.
- A possessive noun shows who or what owns or has something.

Correctly rewrite the letter below.

December 9, 2004

Ms Margaret Wilson
Atlanta Public library
101 Reading Road
Atlanta, Georgia 33560

Dear ms Wilson

I am writing to complain about the poor service in the childrens section of your library. Last saturday, I wanted to check out the North American Snake Guide by Doctor david Howard. I waited for over 30 minute's before anyone came to help me. No ones should have to wait that long.

Yours truly,
Kevin Andrews, Junior

At Home: Have your child write a complaint letter.

© Macmillan/McGraw-Hill

Name_____

A. Decide whether each underlined word is a plural noun or a possessive noun. Then write *plural* or *possessive* on the line provided.

1. This <u>snake's</u> bite is not poisonous. _____

2. Sidewinders leave J-shaped <u>tracks</u> in the sand. _____

3. The <u>teacher's</u> science lesson was very interesting. _____

4. Some <u>reptiles</u> change color to match their surroundings.

   _____

5. We went to see the <u>museum's</u> display. _____

6. I decided to write down some <u>notes</u>. _____

7. The <u>facts</u> are very important. _____

8. That <u>reptile's</u> skin is shiny. _____

B. Choose the plural or possessive noun that best completes each sentence. Write it on the line provided.

9. (Sharks, Shark's) kill fewer people than snakes do. _____

10. She checked out books from two (libraries, library's). _____

11. The (farmers, farmer's) crops were harmed by the insects.

    _____

12. The (colors, color's) of the snakeskin were red, black, and gold.

    _____

13. The (magazines, magazine's) articles were very helpful. _____

14. Don't touch those (animals, animals') skeletons! _____

15. Several (people, people's) stopped by the exhibit. _____

Name_____

Mechanics

- Add -s to most nouns to form the plural. Do not use an apostrophe.
- Add an apostrophe and -s to a singular noun to make it possessive.

Read the sentences about the picture below. Then find the plural and possessive nouns that are not written correctly. Rewrite the sentences on the lines below, correcting the plural or possessive nouns.

1. What does this pages picture show you?

_____

2. My two friend both like to read a lot.

_____

3. I went to the schools Web site on the computer.

_____

4. Emily is using these three article's for her research paper.

_____

Read each passage. Choose a word or group of words that belong in each space. Circle your answer.

_____ pitching was amazing. She even struck out
(1)

_____!
(2)

1. **A** Jackie
   B Jackies'
   C Jackie's
   D Jackies

2. **F** Mister Babe ruth
   G Mr. Babe Ruth
   H Mr Babe Ruth
   J Mr. babe Ruth

The move to New York was exciting. We spent weeks packing our
_____. When we got there, the first place I wanted to visit
(3)

was the _____.
(4)

3. **A** boxes
   B boxs
   C box's
   D boxies

4. **F** New york Public Library
   G New York Public Library
   H New York public library
   J New York Public library

On our trip to China, there were so many sights to see! We visited
_____. We took a bus tour with a group of forty
(5)

_____.
(6)

5. **A** Hong kong, Beijing
   and the Great Wall
   B Hong Kong Beijing
   and the Great Wall
   C Hong Kong, Beijing,
   and the great Wall
   D Hong Kong, Beijing,
   and the Great Wall

6. **F** mans and womans
   G mens and womens
   H men and women
   J men's and women's

Many _____ have improved our world. Some people invent
         (7)

ways to improve other people's inventions. For example, Lewis Latimer

found a way to improve _____.
                                (8)

7.
A inventor's creations
B inventor creations
C inventors' creations
D inventors creation's

8.
F Edisons electric lights
G Edison electric light's
H Edison's electric lights'
J Edison's electric lights

_____ snakes include the ribbon snake and the indigo.
         (9)

The ribbon _____ make it look like a brightly colored
                        (10)

ribbon.

9.
A North America's
B north America's
C North Americas'
D North Americas

10.
F snakes stripe's
G snake's stripes
H snake's stripes'
J snakes' stripes

Name_____

> • An **action verb** tells what the subject does or did.
> • A verb in the **present-tense** tells what happens now.
> • The present-tense must have **subject-verb agreement**. Add -s to most verbs if the subject is singular. Do not add -s if the subject is plural or I or you.

Write the correct present-tense form of each underlined verb on the lines provided.

1. The roadrunner <u>race</u> across the empty desert. _____

2. He <u>pause</u> near the ribbon of highway. _____

3. A car <u>speed</u> down the road. _____

4. The passengers <u>looks</u> out the window. _____

5. They <u>stares</u> at the roadrunner. _____

6. The roadrunner <u>take</u> off again. _____

7. A lizard <u>jump</u> into a hole to escape the roadrunner. _____

8. The wind <u>blow</u> the roadrunner's feathers. _____

9. Two hares <u>hops</u> out of the roadrunner's way. _____

10. The roadrunner <u>shake</u> its long tail. _____

At Home: Have your child write three sentences about roadrunners. Have him or her circle the verbs in their sentences.

Roadrunner's Dance
Grade 4/Unit 3
65

Name_____

> • Add -*es* to verbs that end in *s, ch, sh, x,* or *z* if the subject is singular.
> • Change *y* to *i* and add -*es* to verbs that end with a consonant and *y*.
> • Do not add -*s* or -*es* to a present-tense verb when the subject is plural or *I* or *you*.

Read each sentence. Write the correct present-tense form of each underlined verb on the lines provided.

1. The rattlesnake <u>stretch</u> out along the rocks. _____

2. His scales <u>flashes</u> silver in the hot desert sun. _____

3. He <u>swish</u> his long tail. _____

4. A prairie dog <u>scurry</u> away when it hears the snake's rattle.

   _____

5. A small lizard <u>crawl</u> away. _____

6. The rattlesnake <u>reach</u> the edge of the rock. _____

7. A bee <u>buzz</u> past the snake. _____

8. The rattlesnake <u>hurry</u> down the rock. _____

9. He quickly <u>pass</u> by a cold, shaded area. _____

10. You <u>approaches</u> any snake with caution. _____

© Macmillan/McGraw-Hill

At Home: Have your child choose three verbs from this page. Have him or her write a sentence for each verb.

- Use quotation marks at the beginning and end of a speaker's exact words.
- Begin a quotation with a capital letter.
- Do not use quotation marks when you do not use the speaker's exact words.

Rewrite each sentence correctly by putting capital letters and quotation marks where they belong.

1. Roberto asked me, have you ever seen a rattlesnake?

_____

2. no, I never have, I answered.

_____

3. roberto told me that rattlesnakes are his favorite animal.

_____

4. Our science teacher said, rattlesnakes are related to lizards.

_____

5. both rattlesnakes and lizards are reptiles, she explained.

_____

6. some reptiles can even change colors! Andrea said.

_____

7. yes, you are thinking of chameleons, Andrea, replied Ms. Giordello.

_____

8. why do they do that? asked Hakim.

_____

© Macmillan/McGraw-Hill

At Home: Have your child write three sentences of dialogue. Ask him or her to use quotations in each sentence.

Name_____

> - The present tense must have subject-verb agreement.
> - Add -s to most verbs if the subject is singular.
> - Add -es to verbs that end in s, ch, sh, x, or z if the subject is singular.
> - Change y to i and add -es to verbs that end in a consonant and -y.

Proofread the dialogue below. Look for mistakes in action verbs and quotations. Rewrite the dialogue, using action verbs and quotations correctly.

I am so excited! Today I lcaves on a trip to Taos, New Mexico! Carla say.

Dad reply, we should be there in an hour.

Mom point to the mountains in the distance. She say, stop the car so we can takes some pictures.

Carla remark, I see a strange bird.

Dad explain, the bird is a roadrunner.

Carla watch the speedy bird. It pass close enough to see its feathers.

_____

_____

_____

_____

_____

_____

_____

_____

At Home: Ask your child to add two lines of dialogue to the story above.

A. Read each sentence. Circle the letter of the sentence that has correct subject-verb agreement.

1. **a.** The roadrunner comes down from the mountain.

   b. He look at the desert.

   c. The roadrunner speed across the road.

   d. The other animals rushes out of his way.

2. **a.** The rattlesnake slide down the rocks.

   b. He see the roadrunner.

   c. The rattlesnake shake his tail.

   d. The rattles make a hollow clatter.

B. Read each sentence. Circle the letter before the present-tense verb that belongs in the sentence. Make sure the spelling is correct.

3. The roadrunner _____ across the highway.

   a. run

   b. runs

   c. runes

   d. runies

4. The rattlesnake _____ the desert for other animals.

   a. watch

   b. watchs

   c. watches

   d. watchies

© Macmillan/McGraw-Hill

- The present tense must have subject-verb agreement.
- Add -s to most verbs if the subject is singular.
- Add -es to verbs that end in s, ch, sh, x, or z if the subject is singular.
- Change y to i and add -es to verbs that end in a consonant and -y.

Mechanics

- Use quotation marks at the beginning and end of the speaker's exact words.
- Begin a quotation with a capital letter.
- Do not use quotation marks when you do not use the speaker's exact words.

Rewrite each sentence correctly, paying attention to the present-tense verb and quotation rules. Then use the information in the sentences to draw the missing part of the picture.

1. Mr. Duncan suggest, let's tell a story about a roadrunner.

_____

2. the roadrunner dash across the desert, Gary say.

_____

3. Shanita joke, it's headed for New Mexico!

_____

4. Alissa add, the rattlesnakes watches it from behind cactuses.

_____

Name_____

- A verb in the **past tense** tells about an action that has already happened.
- Add -ed to most verbs to show past tense.
- If a verb ends with e, drop the e and add -ed.
- If a verb ends with a consonant and y, change y to i and add -ed.
- If a verb ends with one vowel and one consonant, double the consonant and add -ed.

Choose a verb for each sentence. Write the verb in the past tense.

1. We _____ Martin Luther King, Jr.'s birthday in January. (celebrate, irritate)

2. People _____ home from school for the holiday. (visit, stay)

3. The students in our school _____ about Dr. King before the holiday. (learn, earn)

4. We _____ a program of events about Dr. King. (repair, prepare)

5. Today my class _____ a play about his childhood. (perform, inform)

6. James _____ the lead in the show. (play, place)

7. He _____ his lines before going onstage. (prevent, practice)

8. He _____ his Aunt Betty to come to the play. (sag, beg)

9. Our teacher, Mrs. Clark, _____ us good luck before the play started. (wish, wash)

10. We all _____ our best to make the show a success. (cry, try)

At Home: Have your child write five sentences using the past tense of the verbs he or she didn't choose in the above sentences.

Name_____

> • A verb in the **future tense** tells about an action that is going to happen.
> • To write about the future, use the special verb *will*.

Underline the action verb in each sentence. Rewrite the sentence so it tells about the future.

1. The teachers assign a project about the Civil Rights movement.

_____

2. The students work in pairs.

_____

3. All of the classes go to the library.

_____

4. Cordell and Janine find out about the Voting Rights Act of 1965.

_____

5. Yvonne and Frank learn about educational rights.

_____

6. The librarians show us the right books and magazines.

_____

7. Juan and Patricia give an oral report.

_____

8. Josie and Emmett create a poster.

_____

At Home: Ask your child to write four sentences about something he or she wants to learn in the future.

Name _____

- The present tense must have subject-verb agreement. Add -s to most verbs if the subject is singular. Do not add -s if the subject is plural or *I* or *you*.
- Add -es to verbs that end in s, ch, sh, x, or z if the subject is singular. Do not add -es when the subject is plural or *I* or *you*.
- For past-tense verbs, use the same form for singular and plural subjects.
- For future-tense verbs, use the same form for singular and plural subjects.

Pick the correct form of the verb in each sentence below. Underline your answer.

1. Ms. Harkner's class (take, takes) a field trip today.

2. The students (will visit, will visits) the Martin Luther King, Jr. Historic Site.

3. The class (hurry, hurries) to the buses at 9:00 A.M.

4. The buses (reach, reaches) Atlanta at 10:00 A.M.

5. Tour guides (show, shows) us through Martin Luther King's birth home.

6. A guide (teach, teaches) us about Martin Luther King, Jr.'s childhood.

7. Dr. King and his family (lived, liveds) in Alabama.

8. Dr. King (delivered, delivereds) the "I Have a Dream" speech in 1963.

9. My parents and I (will discuss, will discusses) the field trip tonight.

10. My sister's class (will tour, will tours) the site next week.

© Macmillan/McGraw-Hill

At Home: Have your child choose any three sentences above and rewrite them using a different verb tense.

Name_____

- A verb in the past tense tells about an action that has already happened.
- A verb in the future tense tells about an action that is going to happen.

Rewrite the poem below. Be sure to correct any mistakes in subject-verb agreement.

Just History?

To me, it's a mystery —
Why do people thinks
Dr. King is just history?
He stand on the brink
of a change. He dream
of equality. He speak
with calm strength. His world seem
cold, but he seek
to warm it. Dr. King, we will remembers
you.

_____

_____

_____

_____

_____

_____

_____

At Home: Have your child write a short poem in response to the reading selection.

A. Rewrite each underlined verb, using the correct past-tense form.

1. Gordon <u>help</u> Ms. Morrison decorate the classroom. _____

2. The students <u>copy</u> quotes from Dr. King onto big banners. _____

3. Gordon <u>place</u> a banner on the wall. _____

4. The corner of the banner <u>flap</u> in the breeze. _____

5. The teacher <u>push</u> a pin into each corner of the banner. _____

B. Choose a verb from the box below to complete each sentence. Write the correct future-tense form of the verb.

| fix | invite | tape | wish | worry |

6. I _____ the sign to the wall.

7. The sign _____ people to our Martin Luther King, Jr. celebration.

8. Anna _____ that the sign isn't straight.

9. Ms. Morrison _____ the sign for us.

10. Our class _____ visitors welcome as they walk into the room.

Name_____

- Add -ed to most verbs to show past tense.
- If a verb ends with e, drop the e and add -ed.
- If a verb ends with a consonant and y, change y to i and add -ed.
- If a verb ends with one vowel and one consonant, double the consonant and add -ed.
- To write about the future, use the special verb will.

Mechanics

- For past- and future-tense verbs, use the same form for singular and plural subjects.

**Change each underlined verb
to the correct past or future tense.**

Last November, Jena <u>work</u> _____ on her project for social

studies. During that month, her class <u>study</u> _____ the life of

Dr. Martin Luther King, Jr. Jena <u>construct</u> _____ a collage. She

went through magazines and <u>clip</u> _____ pictures and words. She

<u>arrange</u> _____ the words into quotations on a big piece of paper.

Her school <u>present</u> _____ an art show on the Civil Rights

movement next February. Jena <u>show</u> _____ her collage there.

Teachers, students, and parents <u>attend</u> _____.

Name_____

- The **main verb** in a sentence shows what the subject does or is.
- A **helping verb** helps the main verb show an action or make a statement.
- *Have, has, had, is, are, am, was, were,* and *will* are helping verbs.
- *Is, are, am, was,* and *were* can be used with a main verb ending in *-ing.* A verb in the **past tense** tells about an action that has already happened.
- *Will* is a helping verb used to show an action in the future.

Draw one line under each helping verb. Draw two lines under each main verb.

1. Gidget always has liked to help others.

2. Next year, she will volunteer at the homeless shelter.

3. The shelter workers have decided that for now, she is too young.

4. Gidget has considered other ways to help.

5. She is starting her own group.

6. Gidget and her group are collecting things for homeless kids.

7. As of last week, they had gathered jackets, school supplies, and backpacks.

8. I am thinking of joining the group.

9. Yesterday we were talking about the group.

10. When I tell my friends, I am sure they will help too.

At Home: Have your child write three sentences using helping verbs about ways he or she helps others.

Name _____

- The **main** verb in a sentence shows what the subject does or is.
- A **helping verb** helps the main verb show an action or make a statement.
- *Have, has,* and *had* can be helping verbs.
- *Is, are, am, was, were,* and *will* can be helping verbs.

Write a main verb or helping verb to complete each sentence.

1. Charlie _____ searched for a place to volunteer.

2. He has _____ lists of groups.

3. Charlie _____ worrying about choosing the right place to help.

4. He _____ visit different groups.

5. The people in the soup kitchen are _____ vegetables.

6. Many people _____ donated clothes to this group.

7. This afternoon Charlie is _____ for people who couldn't leave their homes.

8. He has _____ floors at the animal shelter.

9. Charlie _____ pitch in wherever he can.

10. The leaders of the groups are _____ him and telling him he's done a great job.

At Home: Have your child read paragraphs in a favorite book. Ask your child to write down five combinations of main and helping verbs.

Name_____

- A **contraction** is a shortened form of two words.
- A contraction can be made by combining certain verbs with the word *not.*
- An apostrophe (') shows that the letter *o* has been left out.
- Examples of contractions: *is + not = isn't, did + not = didn't*

Read each sentence. Write the contraction for each set of underlined words.

1. Annie <u>has not</u> finished sorting the bags of donated clothes.

   _____

2. Chris <u>is not</u> making cookies for himself, but will sell them at the bake sale. _____

3. Gina <u>does not</u> use these toys anymore, so she will donate them.

   _____

4. Stacy and Steven will help too, because they <u>are not</u> selfish.

   _____

5. Sam <u>could not</u> make it to the bake sale, but he raked leaves at the park. _____

6. We <u>should not</u> bring toys to the hospital after 8 P.M. _____

7. Carlos enjoyed his work at the soup kitchen so much that he <u>did not</u> want to leave. _____

8. Amy and Alex <u>do not</u> work at the animal shelter on Thursdays.

   _____

9. Karen and Stanley <u>have not</u> decided yet where to volunteer.

   _____

10. The volunteers <u>were not</u> needed at the nursing home today.

   _____

At Home: Write down the contractions from this page. Ask your child to give the longer forms.

Name

- The main verb in a sentence shows what the subject does or is.
- A helping verb helps the main verb show an action or make a statement. Add *-ed* to most verbs to show past-tense.
- *Have, has,* and *had* can be helping verbs.
- *Is, are, am, was, were,* and *will* can be helping verbs.

Rewrite the paragraphs below. Be sure to correct any main verbs, helping verbs, or contractions that are used incorrectly.

Everyone should volunteering to help others. It does'nt matter what you do. Any way you can help will makes a difference. You don'ot have to give up all of your free time. You can help even by volunteering just a few hours a week. Many local organizations are count on volunteers.

One way you can help is by working at a soup kitchen. Starting on Wednesday, I will work at the soup kitchen on Fifth Street. I'm look forward to it.

If you take time to help others, you will knowed that you has made your community a better place.

_____

_____

_____

_____

_____

_____

_____

© Macmillan/McGraw-Hill

At Home: Have your child add three sentences to the paragraphs above about a way in which he or she could volunteer.

A. Read each sentence. Draw one line under the helping verb and two lines under the main verb.

1. The class has planned a pancake breakfast for a fundraiser.

2. They are hoping to raise money to help children in homeless shelters.

3. The students have invited everyone they know.

4. Casey and Jerome are mixing milk, eggs, and butter.

5. Scott is pouring batter on the griddle.

B. Choose the correct helping verb to complete each sentence. Write it on the line.

6. Anya _____ flipping pancakes like an expert.
   a. am
   b. are
   c. was

7. Gordy and Fred _____ pitching in by showing people to their seats.
   a. was
   b. are
   c. is

8. The class probably _____ succeeded in raising money.
   a. will
   b. have
   c. has

Name_____

- The **main verb** in a sentence shows what the subject does or is.
- A **helping verb** helps the main verb show an action or make a statement. Add *-ed* to most verbs to show past tense.

Mechanics

- A **contraction** is a shortened form of two words.
- A contraction can be made by combining certain verbs with the word *not*.
- An apostrophe (') shows that the letter *o* has been left out.
- Examples of contractions: *is + not = isn't, did + not = didn't*

Look at the picture. Circle the mistakes in main verbs and helping verbs. Change the underlined words to contractions.

    Mr. Ramsey's class has reading about the work Gidget Schultz did for homeless children. The students also wants to help people.

    The students is visiting stores in town and explain their idea. The stores has invited them to pick out what they want. The class is shopped for notebooks, crayons, backpacks, and other supplies. The store owners

are not _____ charging the students for these items. Later, the whole class will drops them off at the homeless shelter. Children who

did not _____ have school supplies will having them.

© Macmillan/McGraw-Hill

> • A linking verb does not show action. It connects the subject to the rest of the sentence.
> • *Is, are, am, was,* and *were* are often used as linking verbs.

Read each sentence. Study the linking verbs in parentheses. Write the form of the linking verb that correctly completes each sentence.

1. The story we read (was, were) _____ Mystic Horse.

2. It (is, are) _____ about the Native American Pawnee tribe.

3. My classmates (was, were) _____ excited to learn more about this tribe.

4. Our school field trips (is, are) _____ next month.

5. The Natural History Museum (is, are) _____ the place we will visit.

6. The museum's exhibit on the Plains Native Americans (is, are) _____ wonderful.

7. The Pawnee, Omaha, and Oto tribes (was, were) _____ Plains tribes.

8. I (am, are) _____ Native American on my mother's side of the family.

9. Reading the tribes' own words and stories (is, are) _____ the best way to learn their history.

10. The stories (is, are) _____ fascinating to me.

At Home: Ask your child to write a paragraph about the story. Have your child use linking verbs in his or her paragraphs.

Mystic Horse • Grade 4/Unit 3   **83**

- A linking verb does not show action. It connects the subject to the rest of the sentence.
- *Is, are, am, was,* and *were* are often used as linking verbs.
- Some linking verbs link the subject to a noun in the predicate.
- Some linking verbs link the subject to an adjective in the predicate.

Complete each sentence by writing the correct linking verb on the line. Then underline the complete subject of the sentence.

1. Our social studies project _____ an interesting assignment.

2. I _____ eager to get started on it.

3. The Pawnee tribe _____ the subject of my project.

4. <u>Mystic Horse</u> _____ my favorite book last year.

5. The Pawnee Indians _____ unfamiliar to me before I read that book.

6. They _____ a group I want to learn more about now.

7. The state of Nebraska _____ the place the Pawnee lived long ago.

8. Many books about the Pawnee _____ in the school library.

9. The library _____ so big that I can't always find what I need.

10. Our librarian, Ms. Kribble, _____ helpful to students.

At Home: Write *is, are, am, was,* and *were* on index cards. Have your child pick a card and use each verb in a sentence orally.

Name_____

- In a play, use a **colon** (:) between each character's name and his or her words.
- Do not use quotation marks around dialogue in a play.
- Start a new line each time a new character is speaking.
- Use **parentheses** ( ) around stage directions. These are directions that tell what characters do on stage or how they say their words out loud.
  Example: GEORGE (*loudly*): It's right here, Mr. Taylor! (*George holds up the book.*)

Rewrite each line of dialogue below. Add colons and parentheses where they are needed.

1. MR. BRYANT *cheerfully*. "Class, we are going to act out a story in our reading book." *MR. BRYANT smiles.*

   _____

   _____

2. OLIVIA *calling out*. "Which story will we do, Mr. Bryant?" *OLIVIA waves her hand wildly in the air.*

   _____

   _____

3. MR. BRYANT. "Which story do you think will make a good play?" *MR. BRYANT shrugs his shoulders.*

   _____

   _____

4. CARLOS *slowly*. "How about <u>Mystic Horse,</u> Mr. Bryant? The whole class loved that book."

   _____

   _____

At Home: Have your child add a line of dialogue to the scene above. Tell your child to include a stage direction.

- A linking verb does not show action. It connects the subject to the rest of the sentence.
- *Is, are, am, was,* and *were* are often used as linking verbs.
- Some linking verbs link the subject to a noun in the predicate.
- Some linking verbs link the subject to an adjective in the predicate.

Rewrite the lines of this play. Correct any linking verbs that are used incorrectly. Be sure to use proper punctuation for a play.

T.J. "I need an idea for my social studies project. I can't think of anything."
T.J. paces the room nervously.
CARA *confidently.* "My project are about Pawnee folktales."
T.J. "That's a good idea, Cara." *CARA opens the book and points to a picture.*
CARA. "The Plains tribes is very interesting to read about."
T.J. *excitedly.* "This were a great idea."

_____

_____

_____

_____

_____

_____

_____

_____

_____

At Home: Have your child find samples of dialogue in books. Take turns reading the dialogue aloud.

A. Find the linking verb in each sentence. Write it on the line.

1. The college my sister Sharon goes to is in Nebraska. _____

2. Sharon and her friends were hard workers in high school.

_____

3. Even when she was little, she was interested in the Pawnee tribe.

_____

4. Pawnee folktales are part of what she studies in college.

_____

B. Find the noun or adjective in the predicate that is linked to the subject by a linking verb. Write the noun or adjective on the line.

5. Pedro's favorite book is <u>Mystic Horse</u>. _____

6. The lives of the Plains Indians were different from ours.

_____

7. Dr. Gonzalez and Dr. Lasser are experts on the Pawnee tribe.

_____

8. Pedro's report on the Plains Indians was very detailed.

_____

- A linking verb does not show action. It connects the subject to the rest of the sentence.
- Some linking verbs link the subject to a noun in the predicate.
- Some linking verbs link the subject to an adjective in the predicate.

Read the following lines from a play. Rewrite the lines, correcting any mistakes in linking verbs. Be sure to punctuate the lines correctly.

MOM. "On Saturday, we leave for a road trip."

FRAN. "I is curious about where we are going."

MOM. "We're going to Nebraska. The museum there are a great place to find information about the Pawnee. My next book am about the Pawnee."

FRAN. "My class studied the Pawnee tribe last year!"

_____

_____

_____

_____

_____

_____

_____

_____

Name_____

> • An irregular verb is a verb that does not add -ed to form the past tense.

Write the correct past-tense form of the underlined verb on the line provided.

1. The snow <u>begin</u> _____ to fall.

2. The sunlight <u>make</u> _____ the snow and ice glitter.

3. An icicle <u>break</u> _____ off the roof.

4. I <u>find</u> _____ the icicle on the ground.

5. The first snow <u>come</u> _____ earlier than usual this year.

6. We <u>go</u> _____ to the pond to ice-skate.

7. Elijah and I <u>do</u> _____ leaps, twists, and turns on the ice.

8. He <u>fly</u> _____ through the air and landed safely on the blades of his skates.

9. Nina <u>draw</u> _____ a picture of the frozen pond.

10. We decided to go home when we <u>see</u> _____ it was getting dark.

At Home: Have your child write three sentences about winter, using the past-tense form of an irregular verb.

Name_____

> • Some irregular verbs have special spellings when used with the helping verbs *have, has,* or *had.*

Read each sentence and the verb choices in parentheses. Underline the verb choice that correctly completes the sentence.

1. Alice has (did, done) many drawings and photographs of the park in winter.

2. She had (make, made) it a hobby by the time she was ten years old.

3. For the past four years, her parents have (given, gave) her a photo album each year for her birthday.

4. Alice has carefully (put, putted) all of her winter pictures in the albums.

5. Today, the surface of the pond has (frozen, froze).

6. Alice took pictures of the tree because she had (saw, seen) icicles on it.

7. She has (lay, laid) her camera aside while she gets more film out of her bag.

8. By the end of the afternoon, the icicles have (shrunk, shrank) in the sun.

9. Before she went home, Alice had (taken, took) more than 40 pictures.

10. The next morning, she saw that more snow had (fell, fallen).

At Home: Ask your child to rewrite the above sentences using past-tense verbs without using *have, has,* or *had.*

Name_____

> - An **irregular verb** is a verb that does not add *-ed* to form the past tense.
> - Some irregular verbs have special spellings when used with the helping verbs *have, has,* or *had*.

Rewrite each sentence with the correct form of the underlined verb. For each sentence, use the form that makes better sense— the past-tense form or the past with the helping verb *have, has,* or *had*.

1. We <u>go</u> outside an hour ago.

_____

2. It has <u>grow</u> colder since we have been outside.

_____

3. I <u>know</u> it was a good idea to wear my gloves, hat, and scarf.

_____

4. The snow and ice have <u>hide</u> the roots of the trees.

_____

5. The path <u>lead</u> us straight to the forest.

_____

6. I <u>keep</u> my hands in my pockets.

_____

7. We had <u>choose</u> the first day of winter to take pictures of the forest.

_____

8. The winds have <u>blow</u> drifts of snow against the bare trees.

_____

At Home: Make a chart with two columns labeled *Past Tense* and *Past with Have, Has, or Had*. Have your child fill in the columns.

Snowflake Bentley

Grade 4/Unit 3

91

- An irregular verb is a verb that does not add *-ed* to form the past tense.
- Some irregular verbs have special spellings when used with the helping verbs *have, has,* or *had.*

Rewrite the character sketch below. Be sure to correct any mistakes in the use of irregular verbs.

Margaret

Margaret getted up early this morning. She bringed her camera to the pond. She taked a picture of a fish before it swimmed away. She photographed geese as they fly south for the winter. Soon she had took dozens of pictures.

Ever since she was a little girl, Margaret had know she wanted to be a photographer. By the age of 15, she had winned three photography awards. Now 30 years old, she has write a guide for beginning photographers. She has maked photography her life's work.

_____

_____

_____

_____

_____

_____

_____

_____

_____

_____

At Home: Have your child add a sentence to the description of Margaret. Ask your child to include irregular past-tense verbs.

Name_____

A. Circle the letter before the irregular verb that correctly completes each sentence.

1. Kevin _____ his camera and picked it up.
   a. find
   b. finded
   c. found
   d. founded

2. Laurie has _____ some sketches of the snow-covered trees.
   a. draw
   b. drew
   c. draw
   d. drawn

B. Circle the letter before the correct irregular verb and helping verb that completes each sentence.

3. The weather _____ colder and windier since this morning.
   a. has become
   b. have become
   c. has became
   d. have became

4. Before she retired, the professor _____ a career out of studying snowflakes.
   a. has maded
   b. has make
   c. had make
   d. had made

Name_____

- An irregular verb is a verb that does not add *-ed* to form the past tense.
- Some irregular verbs have special spellings when used with the helping verbs *have, has,* or *had.*

Read the sentences about the picture below. Change the verbs that are not written correctly. Rewrite the sentences on the lines below.

1. All day long, the snow had fallen.

_____

2. After school, we runned outside to play in the snow.

_____

3. Carter has catched a snowflake on his tongue.

_____

4. Lisa throwed a snowball into the pond.

_____

5. Jordan and Chris have builded a snowman.

_____

Read the passage and look at the underlined parts. Is there a better way to write and say each part? If there is, which is the better way? Circle your answer.

(1) The rattlesnakes shakes their tails. The tails make a noise. (2) The children hushes as the teacher says, Listen! The class will learn more about rattlesnakes at the museum.

1. A. The rattlesnakes shake their tails.
   B. The rattlesnakes shakies their tails.
   C. The rattlesnakes shakeses their tails.
   D. No mistake

2. F. The children hushs as the teacher says, "Listen!"
   G. The children hush as the teacher says, Listen!
   H. The children hush as the teacher says, "Listen!"
   J. No mistake

(3) The students studyd Martin Luther King, Jr. in social studies class. They admired his efforts in the Civil Rights movement. (4) They will learns more about him next week.

3. A. The students studyed Martin Luther King, Jr., in social studies class.
   B. The students studyied Martin Luther King, Jr., in social studies class.
   C. The students studied Martin Luther King, Jr., in social studies class.
   D. No mistake

4. F. They learn more about him next week.
   G. They will learn more about him next week.
   H. They will learned more about him next week.
   J. No mistake

Name

Do you do any volunteer work? (5) <u>My brother and I is volunteer at a local</u> <u>hospital.</u> Our parents have always encouraged us to help others. (6) <u>We</u> <u>havn't yet told them about our new volunteer jobs.</u>

5. **A.** My brother and I are volunteering at a local hospital.
　　B. My brother and I are volunteered at a local hospital.
　　C. My brother and I is volunteering at a local hospital.
　　D. No mistake

6. **F.** We have'nt yet told them about our new volunteer jobs.
　　G. We havent' yet told them about our new volunteer jobs.
　　H. We haven't yet told them about our new volunteer jobs.
　　J. No mistake

(7) <u>My sister is the author of a play.</u> It is about the Pawnee tribe. (8) <u>Her</u> <u>plays is usually very exciting and dramatic.</u> I always enjoy acting in them.

7. **A.** My sister are the author of a play.
　　B. My sister be the author of a play.
　　C. My sister am the author of a play.
　　D. No mistake

8. **F.** Her plays are usually very exciting and dramatic.
　　G. Her plays was usually very exciting and dramatic.
　　H. Her plays were usually very exciting and dramatic.
　　J. No mistake

Last month, we went to the mountains. (9) <u>Snow falled all week long.</u> We learned to ski and snowboard. (10) <u>When we had went the year before, there</u> <u>hadn't been as much snow.</u>

9. **A.** Snow fall all week long.
　　B. Snow felled all week long.
　　C. Snow fell all week long.
　　D. No mistake

10. **F.** When we had go the year before, there hadn't been as much snow.
　　G. When we had gone the year before, there hadn't been as much snow.
　　H. When we gone the year before, there hadn't been as much snow.
　　J. No mistake

- A **pronoun** is a word that takes the place of one or more nouns.
- A pronoun must match the noun it refers to.
- Singular pronouns are *I, you, he, she, it, me, him,* and *her.*
- Plural pronouns are *we, you, they, us,* and *them.*

Underline the incorrect pronoun in each sentence. Then write the correct pronoun on the line provided.

1. There was no apple cake left because the dog ate them. _____

2. Mrs. Hibbins says her cats are angels, but he are not. _____

3. Why doesn't he send her own dog to obedience school? _____

4. Ask the dogs to please be quiet because he am trying to sleep.

   _____

5. I feel sick, and I don't know what's wrong with I. _____

6. My brother and I hope that us can get a dog. _____

7. When Mrs. LaRue throws the ball, the dog will fetch it for she.

   _____

8. Ike said that him wanted to come home. _____

9. Mrs. LaRue said that her would throw a party for Ike. _____

10. When Mrs. LaRue and Ike were together again, them were very

    happy. _____

11. There were enough cupcakes for all of we. _____

12. Sue asked me to give the ball to she. _____

At Home: Have your child find three sentences from the story that include pronouns.

Dear Mrs. LaRue • **Grade 4/Unit 4** (97)

Name⎯⎯⎯⎯⎯⎯⎯⎯⎯⎯⎯⎯⎯⎯⎯⎯⎯⎯⎯⎯⎯⎯

- A **pronoun** is a word that takes the place of one or more nouns.
- A pronoun must match the noun it refers to.
- Singular pronouns are *I, you, he, she, it, me, him,* and *her.*
- Plural pronouns are *we, you, they, us,* and *them.*

Write the pronoun that correctly replaces the underlined noun in each sentence.

1. At first, Roy didn't want to go to the nursing home because <u>Roy</u> thought the place was boring. ⎯⎯⎯⎯⎯⎯⎯⎯⎯⎯

2. Mrs. Allen said <u>Mrs. Allen</u> found out that dogs were allowed in the nursing home. ⎯⎯⎯⎯⎯⎯⎯⎯⎯⎯

3. Roy knew Grandpa would be happy to see Buddy, so Roy decided to bring <u>Buddy</u>. ⎯⎯⎯⎯⎯⎯⎯⎯⎯⎯

4. The receptionist at the nursing home said to Roy, "I see <u>Roy</u> brought a friend today." ⎯⎯⎯⎯⎯⎯⎯⎯⎯⎯

5. Mrs. Allen said, "<u>Mrs. Allen</u> got Buddy's medical records this morning." ⎯⎯⎯⎯⎯⎯⎯⎯⎯⎯

6. Grandpa said, "I'm glad you brought Buddy to <u>Grandpa</u>."

⎯⎯⎯⎯⎯⎯⎯⎯⎯⎯

7. Grandpa asked <u>Martha</u> if Buddy was allowed in the nursing home. ⎯⎯⎯⎯⎯⎯⎯⎯⎯⎯

8. Another man saw Buddy and said he had a dog that looked like <u>Buddy</u>. ⎯⎯⎯⎯⎯⎯⎯⎯⎯⎯

9. You can treat high blood pressure if you take medicine for <u>the problem</u>. ⎯⎯⎯⎯⎯⎯⎯⎯⎯⎯

10. Roy threw the ball to Buddy so <u>Buddy</u> could fetch it. ⎯⎯⎯⎯⎯⎯⎯⎯⎯⎯

At Home: Have your child write a short paragraph about a pet. Help your child circle the pronouns.

Name_____

- A **pronoun** is a word that takes the place of one or more nouns.
- A pronoun must match the noun it refers to.
- Singular pronouns are *I, you, he, she, it, me, him,* and *her.*
- The pronoun I must always be capitalized.
- Plural pronouns are *we, you, they, us,* and *them.*

Write the pronoun that correctly completes each sentence.

1. I said, "_____ think I must take my cat to the vet."

2. I took the leash because I would need _____ to hold the dog.

3. I am brushing my dog Trixie's coat because _____ will be in a show tomorrow.

4. My dog Edward needs medicine. I give it to _____ every morning.

5. Janice's brother gave _____ a picture of their dog Buddy.

6. Fido buried his bone in the yard, but now he can't find

   _____.

7. My sister and _____ threw the stick, and our dog brought it back to us.

8. Fran's mother told us that _____ had a cat when she was little.

9. My cousins called and _____ told me their cat just had kittens.

10. My little brother wanted to feed the dog, so _____ showed him how to do it.

At Home: Ask family members to describe their favorite animals. Have your child write down the pronouns they use.

Name_____

- A **pronoun** is a word that takes the place of one or more nouns.
- A pronoun must match the noun to which it refers.
- Singular pronouns are *I, you, he, she, it, me, him,* and *her*.
- The pronoun *I* must always be capitalized.
- Plural pronouns are *we, you, they, us,* and *them*.

Read the following paragraphs. Circle all the incorrect pronouns. Then rewrite the paragraph, making sure all pronouns are correct and match their nouns.

    Yesterday i went to the store to buy some food for my dog, Jones. Mr. Edwards greeted her when I came through the door.

    She said, "What can me do for you, Sheila?"

    "I need six cans of the Beef and Chicken Special Diet."

    Mr. Edwards added up the prices and said, "The total is $13.50."

    "Me am sorry," I said. "My mother only gave I $10. How much is it if me only buy four cans?"

    "Let's see. It would be $9.00," he said.

    "All right. That solves my problem. She'll only buy four."

_____

_____

_____

_____

_____

_____

_____

At Home: Have your child write a story about a problem he or she has solved. Then ask your child to identify all the pronouns.

© Macmillan/McGraw-Hill

Name

A. **Write the pronoun that can replace the underlined word or words in each sentence.**

1. The dog led <u>the police</u> to the suspect. _____

2. My sister told <u>my brother</u> to walk the dog. _____

3. <u>Sally</u> and her friend tried to give the cat a bath. _____

4. Fido had the ball in his mouth, but he wouldn't give <u>the ball</u> to me.

   _____

5. Edgar and I took his dog around the lake. <u>He and I</u> were both tired

   afterward. _____

6. If <u>the cats</u> don't stop scratching the couch, we'll have to keep the cats

   outside. _____

7. We saw <u>our neighbors</u> across the street. _____

8. I told <u>my sister</u> not to pet the cat. _____

B. **Write the correct pronouns to complete these sentences.**

9. I bought my cats some catnip, but _____ didn't like it.

10. Last year Bruiser was only a puppy, and now _____
    weighs 100 pounds.

11. My sister didn't believe me when _____ told her how mean
    the dogcatcher was.

12. The Ungers' cat has lived with _____ for 16 years.

13. My friend Mary has both a dog and a cat, and _____ loves
    them both equally.

14. Gertrude has grown up and become a vet. Her family is proud of

    _____ .

15. We brought our cat Jane to the beach, but _____ stayed in
    the cage.

16. The dog has lived with _____ for many years.

Name_____

- A **pronoun** is a word that takes the place of one or more nouns.
- A pronoun must match the noun it refers to.
- Singular pronouns are *I, you, he, she, it, me, him,* and *her*.
- Plural pronouns are *we, you, they, us,* and *them*.

Mechanics

- A **contraction** is a shortened form of two words.
- A contraction may be formed by combining a pronoun and a verb.
- An apostrophe (') shows where one or more letters have been left out.

Write what you think each character is saying. Use the contraction given in your sentence.

1. Dog: (I'm)

_____

_____

2. Boy: (you're)

_____

_____

3. Dog: (it's)

_____

_____

4. Boy: (I'll)

_____

_____

- Use a **subject pronoun** as the subject of a sentence.
- *I, you, he, she, it, we* and *they* are subject pronouns.
- Use an **object pronoun** after an action verb or after a word such as *for, at, of, with,* or *to.*
- *Me, you, him, her, it, us,* and *them* are object pronouns.

Underline the incorrect pronouns and write the correct pronouns on the line.

1. The villagers loved the man, and them all missed him when he died. _____

2. Everyday when the man woke, him went to work in his garden. _____

3. Her and me went to the well for water. _____

4. Us are the only ones who really know him. _____

5. Them are the people we met last year. _____

6. The young man feared the blind man would be unkind to he. _____

7. Her grandmother gave she a special gift. _____

8. This is a secret between you and I. _____

9. Blind people use sounds to help they get around. _____

10. The bugs are a bother to she and Grandpa. _____

11. My father handed the hammer to I. _____

12. Don't forget to call we. _____

At Home: Have your child write three sentences with subject pronouns.

The Blind Hunter • **Grade 4/Unit 4** **103**

Name_____

> • Use a **reflexive pronoun** instead of an object pronoun if the subject of the sentence is doing the action to himself or herself.
> • *Myself, yourself, himself, herself, itself, ourselves, themselves,* and *yourselves* are reflexive pronouns.

Fill in the blanks in the sentences below with the correct reflexive pronoun.

1. Be careful and don't hurt _____.

2. After I go swimming, I dry _____ with a towel.

3. Your baby sister can't feed _____.

4. He made _____ dizzy by spinning around and around.

5. Let's give _____ a break and try again later.

6. The bird washed _____ in the puddle.

7. Boys, please get _____ ready for dinner.

8. The gardener shut the door and locked _____ in the shed.

9. My grandfather almost fell, but he caught _____.

10. Look at _____! You're covered in mud!

11. I tried to reach the towel _____.

12. He looked at _____ in the mirror.

13. We can plant that tree _____.

14. My sister cannot feed _____ without some help.

15. You can help _____ to some cookies.

© Macmillan/McGraw-Hill

At Home: Have your child write three sentences using reflexive pronouns.

Name_____

> • Use a **subject pronoun** as the subject of a sentence.
> • Use an **object pronoun** after an action verb or after a word such as *for, at, of, with,* or *to*.

Read the sentences below. Then write the correct pronouns on the lines provided to complete each sentence.

1. My brother and _____ saw a blind woman walking down the street.

2. _____ was using a cane to find her way.

3. When people saw _____ coming, they moved over to let her pass.

4. How does the woman know where _____ is going?

5. It might be hard for _____ to run errands.

6. He told _____ that she might count the steps to her destination.

7. Do you know what _____ think?

8. I think she does _____ by smell.

9. What do _____ mean, by smell?

10. Each street has its own smell, and that's how she tells _____ apart.

11. Do _____ have some extra money?

12. _____ gave my brother some change.

13. _____ could smell the hot dog stand around the corner.

14. This was going to be a good day for _____.

At Home: Ask your child to write three sentences describing something he or she can't see, using one pronoun in each sentence.

The Blind Hunter • **Grade 4/Unit 4** 105

Name_____

- Use a **subject pronoun** as the subject of a sentence.
- *I, you, he, she, it, we* and *they* are subject pronouns.
- Use an **object pronoun** after an action verb or after a word such as *for, at, of, with,* or *to.*
- *Me, you, him, her, it, us,* and *them* are object pronouns.

Read the paragraphs below. Circle every pronoun that is not used correctly.

Someone gave I directions to the museum

You and us need to walk to Maple Street. Then turn right at Oak Street. Mr. Exeter lives there. Him and me go on walks sometimes. If him is in his yard, he will give a big wave to you and I.

When we got to the museum, we saw Mrs. Peters. Her and my dad went to school together. Them often like the same paintings

Rewrite the passage above. Use the correct forms of the pronouns. Be sure to use capital letters and end punctuation correctly.

_____

_____

_____

_____

_____

_____

_____

At Home: Ask your child to write a short paragraph about what it would be like to visit a museum if you can't see.

Name_____

A. Circle the pronoun or pronouns in parentheses that correctly complete each sentence.

1. (He, Him) and the older man went on a journey.

2. I hurt (me, myself) while walking in the woods.

3. I gave (them, they) five feathers from my collection.

4. (Him, He) and I are going hunting.

5. My parents helped (we, us) with the arrows.

6. My brother found the stones (him, himself).

7. (Them, They) are older than what I have.

8. I thought (we, us) were going the other way.

B. Write the pronoun that completes each sentence.

9. He showed _____ how I should plant the seeds.

10. We sent _____ a message, and they sent one back.

11. She likes to watch birds. It's fun for _____.

12. We need to make breakfast—the eggs won't cook _____!

13. He's wise and everyone respects _____.

14. Let's see where _____ is going.

15. You must learn to respect _____.

Name_____

> • Use a **subject pronoun** as the subject of a sentence.
> • *I, you, he, she, it, we* and *they* are subject pronouns.
> • Use an **object pronoun** after an action verb or after a word such as *for, at, of, with,* or *to*.
> • *Me, you, him, her, it, us,* and *them* are object pronouns.

Mechanics

> • Always write the pronoun *I* with a capital letter.
> • Use *I* or *me* last when talking about yourself and another person.

Read each of the sentences below. Then fill in the blanks with the pronoun that completes each of the sentences.

1. My dad likes birds. _____ knows all about _____.

2. He and I watch birds together. _____ do _____ every weekend.

3. My mom doesn't go because _____ thinks _____ is boring.

4. When _____ bring my little sister, my dad carries _____ in a backpack.

5. _____ usually bring my lunch. If my dad is hungry, I share it with _____.

6. When _____ get home, my feet hurt because _____ are very tired.

Name _____

> • A present-tense verb must agree with its subject pronoun.
> • Add -s to most action verbs when you use the pronouns *he*, *she*, and *it*.
> • Do not add -s to an action verb in the present tense when you use the pronouns *I, we, you,* and *they*.

Write the correct form of the underlined action verb to complete each sentence.

1. My car <u>use</u> _____ less gas than yours.

2. Windmills <u>make</u> _____ energy from the wind.

3. Every few years my dad <u>buy</u> _____ a new truck.

4. Fossil fuels <u>pollute</u> _____ the environment.

5. Scientists help people because they <u>look</u> _____ for new ways to make energy.

6. My mom <u>put</u> _____ up solar panels at her job.

7. Ed's sister <u>design</u> _____ hybrid cars.

8. Rasheed <u>know</u> _____ a great deal about electricity.

9. Where I live, we <u>get</u> _____ energy from the river.

10. Peter's grandfather <u>work</u> _____ in an oil field.

11. My uncle <u>ride</u> _____ a bike to work.

12. The burning of coal <u>send</u> _____ soot into the air.

13. We <u>need</u> _____ more twigs to start the fire.

14. Our teacher <u>hike</u> _____ in the mountains.

At Home: Have your child write a short paragraph describing three ways she or he uses energy every day.

Energy: Power Source
Grade 4/Unit 4

109

© Macmillan/McGraw-Hill

Name_____

- The verbs *have* and *be* have special forms in the present tense.

Have		**Be**	
I have	We have	I am	We are
You have	You have	You are	You are
He/She/It has	They have	He/She/It is	They are

Write the correct form of the underlined verb to complete each sentence.

1. I <u>has</u> _____ a way to tell which house is yours.

2. Your house <u>have</u> _____ six solar panels on its roof.

3. We <u>has</u> _____ had them since last year.

4. They <u>be</u> _____ helping us save energy.

5. They <u>have</u> _____ already saved us some money.

6. I <u>be</u> _____ trying to get my friends to get solar panels.

7. I think Fred and Elliot <u>be</u> _____ going to buy some.

8. Bill <u>be</u> _____ helping protect the environment.

9. Helen <u>are</u> _____ good with tools.

10. She <u>have</u> _____ a big truck that she uses on the job.

11. We <u>be</u> _____ building an addition to our house.

12. Dad <u>have</u> _____ to nail the beams.

13. We <u>be</u> _____ putting in two windows.

14. Now you <u>has</u> _____ a good design.

At Home: Have your child write three sentences using a subject pronoun and the appropriate form of *be* or *have*.

Name_____

- A **contraction** is a shortened form of two words.
- A contraction can be made by combining certain verbs with the word *not*.
- An apostrophe (') shows where at least one letter is missing.
- Examples of contractions: *is + not = isn't, did + not = didn't*

Common Contractions:

	am	is	are	have	has	had	will
I	I'm			I've		I'd	I'll
he		he's			he's	he'd	he'll
she		she's			she's	she'd	she'll
it		it's			it's	it'd	it'll
we			we're	we've		we'd	we'll
you			you're	you've		you'd	you'll
they			they're	they've		they'd	they'll

Write the contraction for the underlined words in each sentence.

1. He had never seen a hybrid car before. _____

2. His mom told him, "I think you will like the new car." _____

3. "I am so excited to see it," he said. _____

4. "Let me finish this article and then I will show it to you." _____

5. After a few minutes, she said, "I have just finished. Let's go."

_____

6. "Let's wait for Dad. He will be here around three o'clock."

_____

7. "You are right, Mom. I do like it." _____

8. "It is very special." _____

At Home: Using contractions, have your child write three sentences about something he or she saw for the first time.

Energy: Power Source   111
Grade 4/Unit 4

Name_____

- A present-tense verb must agree with its subject pronoun.
- Add –*s* to most action verbs when you use the pronouns *he, she,* and *it*.
- Do not add –*s* to an action verb in the present tense when you use the pronouns *I, we, you,* and *they*.
- The verbs *have* and *be* have special forms in the present tense.

Rewrite the following story. Be sure all verbs agree with their pronouns.

Working on the North Slope

Right now, I is far from my family. I is working in a place called the North Slope. That is way up in Alaska. I has only been here for about a month, but my friends Steve and Rob has been here for about two years. We is here to build an oil pipeline. A few years ago, they found oil north of here. Now, we is building a pipeline. When it is done, they will be able to put the oil on ships. It will be at least two years before the job are over. I am glad to be working, but I will be happy to see my family again.

_____

_____

_____

_____

_____

_____

_____

 At Home: Ask your child to find three sentences in the story where a contraction is possible.

Name _____

A. Write the correct form of the underlined action verb or verbs in each sentence.

1. My sister love _____ learning about electricity.

2. When she grow _____ up, she want _____ to be an electrician.

3. She know _____ how to use all kinds of tools.

4. She and our dad fixes _____ things around the house.

5. She read _____ books about how things work.

6. Sometimes my sister and I works _____ on projects together.

7. We designs _____ a simple lamp.

8. My sister and I helps _____ dad with projects.

B. Write the correct form of have or be to complete each sentence.

9. I _____ a friend who works on a wind farm.

10. The wind farm _____ on top of a hill.

11. The windmills there _____ very tall.

12. Each windmill _____ three blades.

13. My friend _____ a small office nearby.

14. I _____ going to visit him this weekend.

15. We _____ taking a tour of the wind farm.

16. It _____ miles and miles of land.

- A present-tense verb must agree with its subject pronoun.
- Add -s to most action verbs when you use the pronouns *he, she,* and *it.*
- Do not add -s to an action verb in the present tense when you use the pronouns *I, we, you,* and *they.*
- The verbs *have* and *be* have special forms in the present tense.

Mechanics

- Use quotation marks at the beginning and end of a person's exact words.
- Begin a quotation with a capital letter.
- Begin a new paragraph each time a new person speaks.

Rewrite the following sentences in dialogue form. Correct any problems in pronoun-verb agreement. Be sure to add quotation marks where they belong.

1. Bill, you has a new bike said Liz.

_____

2. Yes. And my sister have a lot of bikes he said.

_____

3. Where is they asked Liz.

_____

4. They is in the garage said Bill.

_____

5. What do she do with them asked Liz.

_____

6. She like to fix them up he said.

_____

Name_____

> • A **possessive pronoun** takes the place of a possessive noun. It shows who or what owns something.
> • Some possessive pronouns are used before nouns (*my, your, his, her, its, our, your, their*).

Rewrite the underlined parts of the sentences using possessive pronouns and nouns.

1. Adelina's father works on a boat, and <u>the grandfather of Adelina</u> does, too. _____

2. The houses in <u>Adelina's</u> village are small. _____

3. The village is busy, and <u>the village's</u> visitors come from all over the world. _____

4. <u>Her family's</u> job is to take people to see the whales. _____

5. The whales come to the village to have <u>the whales'</u> babies.

   _____

6. Adelina's grandfather's stories are fascinating, and <u>the grandfather's</u> job is, too. _____

7. If you go to Adelina's village, be sure to bring <u>the camera that belongs to you.</u> _____

8. Robert learned about La Laguna from <u>Robert's</u> friend Melissa.

   _____

9. Robert and I went there for <u>the vacation we had</u> last winter.

   _____

10. I took a lot of pictures for <u>the photo album that belongs to me.</u>

    _____

At Home: Ask your child to write three sentences using possessive pronouns.

Adelina's Whales • **Grade 4/Unit 4** **115**

Name_____

> • Some **possessive pronouns** can stand alone (*mine, yours, his, hers, its, ours, yours, theirs*)

In each sentence, replace the underlined incorrect possessive pronoun with the correct one on the line provided.

1. That is your boat, but this one is <u>my's</u>. _____

2. <u>Your's</u> is the smaller life-vest, the blue one. _____

3. I don't have my own, but my brother let me use <u>he's</u>. _____

4. You have your oars. Where are <u>my</u>? _____

5. I wanted to ask Mercedes if I could use <u>her's</u>, but she wasn't at home.

   _____

6. We are off, and the whole day is <u>our</u>! _____

7. Paco and Pepe say this beach is <u>they's</u>, but it's not. _____

8. I forgot my lunch, so will you share <u>your</u>? _____

9. Is that cooler <u>her's</u>? _____

10. The fishing shack on the right is <u>he's</u>. _____

11. Should we go to his fishing shack or <u>your</u>? _____

12. That tackle box is not <u>our</u>. _____

13. <u>It's</u> handle is broken. _____

14. That pretty hat is <u>my</u>. _____

15. Those shoes are <u>her's</u>. _____

At Home: Have your child write three sentences using the possessive pronouns: *mine, yours,* and *ours.*

Name_____

- Add an apostrophe and -*s* to a singular noun to make it possessive.
- Add an apostrophe to make most plural nouns possessive.
- Add an apostrophe and -*s* to form the possessive of plural nouns that do not end in -*s*.
- Possessive pronouns do not have apostrophes.

Read the sentences below. Replace the underlined incorrect possessive noun in each sentence with the correct one on the line provided.

1. My <u>friends</u> grandfather was a fisherman. _____

2. A <u>fishermans</u> life is not always easy. _____

3. He must wake with <u>mornings</u> first light. _____

4. Sometimes the <u>waves</u> power tosses his boat. _____

5. The <u>captains'</u> crew must be strong and able. _____

6. They say that grandfather's boat was once lifted up on a <u>whales</u> back.

   _____

7. He could see the <u>animals'</u> great tail behind him. _____

8. The <u>tails'</u> splash against the water frightened him. _____

9. The boat was dropped back into the <u>seas</u> foamy waters.

   _____

10. The <u>whales'</u> great body disappeared below the surface. _____

At Home: Ask your child to write two sentences imagining what a fisherman's life is like. Have your child use possessive pronouns.

Adelina's Whales • **Grade 4/Unit 4** 117

- Some **possessive pronouns** are used before nouns (*my, your, his, her, its, our, your, their*).
- Some **possessive pronouns** can stand alone (*mine, yours, his, hers, its, ours, yours, theirs*).

Rewrite the following paragraph. Be sure all possessive nouns and pronouns are used correctly.

Me name is Robert and this is mine wife, Florence. That's her' given name, but she prefers to be called Fluffy. Let us show you around our's home. Down the hall we have our's offices. The one on the left is mines, and the one on the right is Fluffy's. My office is where we keep our's jewels. They were my mother's. My father bought them for her on he's many trips abroad. He used to travel a lot in order to study whales. On his's trips, he met some of the world's top scientists. Theirs knowledge of whales was amazing.

_____

_____

_____

_____

_____

_____

_____

_____

_____

_____

At Home: Ask your child to write three sentences using one possessive noun or possessive pronoun in each sentence.

Name_____

Circle the letter before the possessive pronoun that correctly completes each sentence.

1. Adelina's village was small, and _____ main street had only a few houses.

   a his
   b our
   c its
   d their

2. The whales came to Mexico to have _____ young.

   a their
   b your
   c my
   d her

3. Although _____ first visit to La Laguna was in June, this year I'm going in January.

   a his's
   b theirs
   c my
   d her

4. Adelina knows the ocean very well, because _____ whole family works on the water.

   a my
   b their
   c our
   d her

5. Pachico made a sign for his business, and _____ letters are large and easy to read.

   a hers
   b their
   c its
   d my

> - Some **possessive pronouns** are used before nouns (*my, your, his, her, its, our, your, their*).
> - Some **possessive pronouns** can stand alone (*mine, yours, his, hers, its, ours, yours, theirs*).

Mechanics

> - Add an apostrophe and an -*s* to a singular noun to make it possessive.
> - Add an apostrophe to make most plural nouns possessive.
> - Add an apostrophe and -*s* to form the possessive of plural nouns that do not end in -*s*.
> - Possessive pronouns do not have apostrophes.

Read the sentences below about a girl who gets swallowed by a whale. Then, rewrite each sentence, replacing the underlined possessive pronouns with possessive nouns.

1. <u>Its</u> mouth was as big as a cave.

   _____

2. In came a great rush of water, washing her down <u>its</u> throat.

   _____

3. <u>Her</u> eyes had to get used to the darkness in the whale's belly.

   _____

4. Soon she saw she was lying in a pile of fish. <u>Their</u> scales were stuck to <u>her</u> whole body.

   _____

5. She knew her father was nearby. She thought she could hear the motor of <u>his</u> boat. She hoped he would rescue her.

   _____

Name

- *Its, their*, and *your* are possessive pronouns.
- *It's, they're*, and *you're* are contractions for *it is, they are,* and *you are*.
- Be careful not to confuse possessive pronouns with contractions that sound the same.

Read each sentence below. Then circle the correct word in parentheses to complete each sentence.

1. If we don't protect the coral reefs, (their, they're) likely to die.

2. If you visit a coral reef, (your, you're) sure to see many wonderful creatures.

3. When you go, remember to bring (your, you're) snorkel.

4. (Its, It's) important to understand that corals are living things.

5. (Their, They're) lives depend on many things being in balance.

6. Because of all the tiny spaces in the Great Barrier Reef, (its, it's) a great place for a fish to hide.

7. (Its, It's) off the coast of Australia.

8. Surely (your, you're) amazed that the Great Barrier is 1,250 miles long.

9. Imagine all the sea life that lives in all (its, it's) cracks and holes.

10. (Your, You're) going to enjoy your visit to the reef.

11. You don't have to dive far to see (its, it's) beauty.

12. Don't forget (your, you're) flippers.

13. Fish stay in (their, they're) own groups.

14. The mother stays with (its, it's) young.

At Home: Ask your child to write three sentences using a homophone pair in each one. For example: *They're their own worst critics.*

At Home in the Coral Reef
Grade 4/Unit 4
121

Name_____

- *Its, their*, and *your* are possessive pronouns.
- *It's, they're*, and *you're* are contractions for *it is, they are*, and *you are*.
- The word *there* means "in that place." It sounds just like *their* and *they're*.

Write the homophone that correctly completes each sentence.

1. their   they're   there

Go to a coral reef and explore the warm, clear waters _____.

2. Its   It's

_____ not uncommon to find corals in many bright colors.

3. their   they're   there

Corals belong to a family of animals, and _____ relatives include jellyfish and anemones.

4. Its   It's

_____ even possible to find corals growing on shipwrecks.

5. its   it's

A sponge eats by pumping water through tiny holes in _____ body.

6. their   they're   there

The bottom of the ocean is a busy place, and many creatures live

_____.

7. your   you're

Which one is _____ favorite: the sea stars, the sand dollars, or the spiny lobsters?

8. their   they're   there

No matter which one is your favorite, _____ all important to life under the sea.

© Macmillan/McGraw-Hill

 At Home: Have your child write sentences that include the homophones *its, it's, your, you're, their, they're, there*.

- An apostrophe takes the place of letters left out of a contraction.
- Possessive pronouns do not have apostrophes.
- Be careful not to confuse possessive pronouns with contractions.

A. Read the pairs of sentences below. Then write the correct form of the underlined incorrect contraction or possessive pronoun on the line.

1. Have you heard about underwater parks? <u>Their</u> places where sea life is

   protected. _____

2. Fish and people both have homes. The ocean is <u>there's</u> and the land is ours.

   _____

3. Clean water is important for sea life. <u>Its</u> like clean air for us.

   _____

4. A lobster's skeleton is on the outside of <u>it's</u> body. Where's <u>you're</u> skeleton?

   _____

5. Do you want to see the reef? <u>Your</u> going to need a snorkel.

   _____

B. Read each sentence below. Then decide if the underlined word in each sentence is a *possessive noun* or a *contraction*. Write your answer on the line provided.

6. The <u>world's</u> oceans are home to thousands of miles of coral reefs.

   _____

7. <u>It's</u> filled with wonders. _____

8. Some people think that coral is a plant, but really <u>it's</u> an animal.

   _____

9. <u>Coral's</u> relatives have soft, jelly-like bodies. _____

10. The hawksbill turtle is one of the <u>reef's</u> many visitors.

    _____

At Home: Have your child choose a singular noun and use it as a possessive noun.

- *Its, their,* and *your* are possessive pronouns.
- *It's, they're,* and *you're* are contractions for *it is, they are,* and *you are*.
- The word *there* means "in that place." It sounds just like *their* and *they're*.

Rewrite each sentence in the following short essay. There are 6 homophone mistakes.

Most people care about there environment and do things to protect it. But places exist here and their that we don't see every day. Its important to take care of them, too. This summer I visited a beautiful coral reef. But a coral reef isn't just a nice place to visit. Its also like a neighborhood. It's millions of cracks and holes are home to many kinds of sea creatures. When I visited their, I learned that people have to take care of the oceans, not just the land.

_____

_____

_____

_____

_____

_____

_____

_____

At Home: Have your child add two sentences to the paragraph. Be sure he or she uses one of the homophones studied in this unit.

Name_____

Read each sentence. Choose either the possessive pronoun or the contraction to complete the sentences.

its	it's

Although coral is hard, _____ made by a soft, jelly-like animal. When the soft animal dies, it leaves behind _____ skeleton, which is called a polyp. Thousands and thousands of corals begin to form a big pile. After a long time, _____ not just a pile, but a coral reef.

your	you're

When _____ swimming underwater, be sure to bring _____ scuba gear and goggles. _____ sure to see many amazing sights there.

their	they're	there

If the water is clear and warm, coral reefs may grow _____ . After the corals of the reefs release _____ eggs, the eggs become baby corals. For a few weeks afterward, _____ floating through the sea, looking for a hard surface. Once _____ near one, they settle _____ . Then _____ growth depends on temperature, salt, and sunlight.

its	it's

When a coral reef forms, _____ like an underwater city. Each tiny plant inside the coral animals contributes _____ colors. When this "city" grows, _____ a home for millions of small sea animals.

Name_____

- *Its, their,* and *your* are possessive pronouns.
- *It's, they're,* and *you're* are contractions for *it is, they are,* and *you are*.
- The word *there* means "in that place." It sounds just like *their* and *they're*.

Mechanics

- An apostrophe takes the place of letters left out of a contraction.
- Possessive pronouns do not have apostrophes.

Use the words above each paragraph to complete the sentences.

its	it's

_____ a challenge for sponges to eat. A sponge must

push seawater through the many holes in _____ body.

The tiny plants and animals in the water are _____ food.

their	they're	there

When I explored underwater, I saw mollusks. Some mollusks have

soft bodies inside _____ hard shells. _____

protected by the thick shells. Some mollusks, such as octopuses,

squirt water from _____ bodies in order to move.

your	you're

Suppose _____ a squid who lives near a coral reef. What

animals would be part of _____ diet?

Read each passage. Then choose the pronoun or contraction that belongs in each space. Circle your answer.

"Mrs. LaRue, everyone thinks the Hibbins's cats are well behaved. But ___(1)___ certainly aren't! I was up all night listening to ___(2)___ fighting. Please take me home!"

1. A. he
   B. they
   C. you
   D. I

2. E. me
   F. you
   G. him
   H. them

Chirobo was a wise man. ___(3)___ would always take time to answer people's questions. Not only was he wise, he was also kind to children. ___(4)___ would tell them stories.

3. A. He
   B. She
   C. They
   D. We

4. E. He
   F. She
   G. They
   H. We

Although many countries rely on fossil fuels, ___(5)___ not a perfect source of energy. The use of oil has led to pollution. Also, some countries, such as Japan, produce very little of ___(6)___ own oil.

5. A. her
   B. hers
   C. theirs
   D. they're

6. E. her
   F. hers
   G. theirs
   H. their

© Macmillan/McGraw-Hill

Laguna San Ignacio is just a little village, but one thing makes it different from any other town. ___(7)___ the only place where giant gray whales spend time with humans. The whales swim near the shore. They lift ___(8)___ heads to look at villagers like Adelina.

7. A. It's
   B. Its
   C. They're
   D. Their

8. E. you're
   F. their
   G. they're
   H. your

It's important to keep track of tides. For example, fishermen need to know when the water will be high enough for ___(9)___ boats to travel out to sea. And tide waters affect animals, too. ___(10)___ responsible for bringing fresh oxygen for some sea animals.

9. A. they're
   B. their
   C. there
   D. theirs

10. E. They're
   F. Their
   G. There
   H. Theirs

- **Adjectives** are words that describe nouns or pronouns. For example, adjectives may tell what a noun or pronoun looks, sounds, smells, tastes, or feels like.
- Adjectives may be placed before a noun or pronoun. Adjectives may come after the words *a*, *an*, and *the*.
- Adjectives may follow a linking verb.
- Use commas to separate three or more adjectives in a series.

Read the sentences below. Write each adjective on the line provided. Some sentences may have more than one adjective.

1. Florida has big mosquitoes. _____

2. Miss Franny wanted a little house with lots of books. _____

3. That short, smart woman is the librarian. _____

4. She feared that she would seem like a silly woman. _____

5. This book is long and difficult. _____

6. The large bear had a strong smell. _____

7. The bear looked dangerous. _____

8. Winn-Dixie had clean, sharp teeth. _____

9. Miss Franny's father was rich. _____

10. When she saw the dog, she let out a loud, high scream. _____

11. The dog was friendly and clean. _____

12. The bookshelves are high. _____

13. Her father had a loud, scratchy voice. _____

14. The road was not steep at all. _____

© Macmillan/McGraw-Hill

At Home: Have your child write three sentences using adjectives.

Name_____

> • **Proper adjectives** are formed from proper nouns.
> • A proper adjective begins with a capital letter.
> • **Common adjectives** are not formed from proper nouns.
>   Do not capitalize common adjectives.

On the line, rewrite each proper adjective correctly.

1. Today I sat and read in the herman w. block room at the library.

   _____

2. I read a book about bears who live in the michigan woods.

   _____

3. I also learned that mosquitoes live in the florida swamps.

   _____

4. I read about a chinese custom of having brides wear red at weddings.

   _____

5. The room had a shelf of books about asian countries.

   _____

6. This library has more books than both pleasantville libraries put together.

   _____

7. I won't miss the chill of minnesota winters.

   _____

8. I lived near the canadian border, where it got very cold.

   _____

9. That reminds me, I want to find a book on eskimo life.

   _____

10. I already read a book on native american tribes.

   _____

At Home: Have your child look through science or social studies books and list any proper adjectives he or she finds.

- Do not use a comma to separate a single adjective from a noun.
- When only two adjectives are used together, separate them with a comma or *and*. Do not use both.
- Use commas to separate three or more adjectives in a series.
- When you are using only two adjectives before a noun, some adjectives do not need to be separated with commas. These adjectives describe color, size, or age: *a woman with **short gray** hair*.
- Do not use commas or *and* to separate a common adjective from a proper adjective: *the **hot Alabama** summers*.

Rewrite each sentence on the line provided. Be sure to punctuate the sentences correctly.

1. The library is just a little, old, house with lots of books.

_____

2. My dog is friendly, and, calm.

_____

3. The bear came out of the wild, Florida forest.

_____

4. The book was long interesting and hard.

_____

5. That snobby, young girl just came into the library.

_____

6. The bear put his big, and black nose in the air.

_____

7. I grew up in a small, town.

_____

8. I enjoyed the bright colorful exciting pictures in this book.

_____

 At Home: Have your child write sentences using multiple adjectives without commas.

- **Adjectives** describe nouns or pronouns.
- **Proper adjectives** are formed from proper nouns.
- A proper adjective begins with a capital letter.
- **Common adjectives** are not formed from proper nouns. Do not capitalize common adjectives.

Rewrite each sentence in the paragraph below. Remember to use commas and *and* correctly with adjectives. Capitalize proper adjectives. Use a separate page if you need to.

The little, bookstore on the corner is different from the huge, Smithville bookstore in town. Both stores have lots of interesting, and exciting books. But that's the only way they are alike. The small, blue, store on the corner is warm dim. It is filled with old and, unusual books. This store is not like the big smithville store. The Smithville store is bright, and cool. It has new, books by famous popular writers. There is even a counter where you can get a hot sweet tasty cup of cocoa.

_____

_____

_____

_____

_____

_____

_____

_____

_____

_____

At Home: Have your child write five practice sentences using adjectives to exchange with a family member.

Name_____

A. Complete each sentence with an adjective from the box below. Remember to capitalize any proper adjectives.

| reddish | atlantic | british | lonely | ohio |

1. My dog gets _____ when he's by himself.
2. I gathered shells on the sandy _____ shore.
3. My dog's hair is long and _____.
4. We live in a little _____ town.
5. The librarian's voice sounded _____.

B. Choose the group of words that best completes each sentence. Circle the letter of your choice.

6. I brought home a _____ kitten.
   a. fluffy, white,
   b. fluffy white

7. The house was _____.
   a. warm and cozy
   b. warm, and cozy

8. Her dog is _____.
   a. large, brown, and shy
   b. large brown and shy

9. This book contains _____ words.
   a. common spanish
   b. common Spanish

10. The car had _____ tags.
    a. yellow New Jersey
    b. yellow, New Jersey

Name_____

- **Adjectives** describe nouns or pronouns.
- **Proper adjectives** are formed from proper nouns.
- A proper adjective begins with a capital letter.
- **Common adjectives** are not formed from proper nouns.
  Do not capitalize common adjectives.

Mechanics

- Do not use a comma to separate a single adjective from a noun.
- When only two adjectives are used together, separate them with a comma or *and*. Do not use both.
- When you are using only two adjectives before a noun, some adjectives do not need to be separated with commas or *and*. These adjectives describe color, size, or age: *a woman with short gray hair*.
- Do not use commas or *and* to separate a common adjective from a proper adjective: *the hot Alabama summers*.
- Use commas to separate three or more adjectives in a series.

Read the sentences below. Then find the adjectives that are not written correctly. Rewrite the sentences on the lines below, correcting any mistakes.

1. A guide dog helped the blind, young, man.

   _____

2. They walked through the sunny arizona city.

   _____

3. The dog stepped over a prickly, cactus.

   _____

4. My dog likes to eat mexican food.

   _____

5. He's a funny kind helpful dog.

   _____

Name

- The words *a*, *an*, and *the* are special adjectives called **articles**.
- Use *a* and *an* with singular nouns.
- Use *a* if the next word starts with a consonant sound.
- Use *an* if the next word starts with a vowel sound.

Complete each sentence by writing the correct article, *a* or *an*.

1. Félipé was _____ spoiled child.

2. He was upset because he had lost _____ arrow.

3. The arrow had landed in _____ well.

4. Ranita the frog had been put under _____ spell.

5. Félipé tried to think of _____ excuse not to keep his promise.

6. He had promised to give Ranita _____ kiss.

7. He was hoping it was all _____ bad dream.

8. _____ wise woman had cast the spell on Ranita.

9. Ranita didn't think _____ brat like Félipé would make a good husband.

10. Pepé's kiss changed her from _____ ugly frog to a beautiful princess.

11. Both Félipé and Ranita refused to get _____ glass of water for Vieja Sabia.

12. The viceroy believed that even _____ important person had to keep his promises.

13. _____ viceroy has many things to be concerned about.

14. Ranita wore _____ old hat that belonged to her grandmother.

© Macmillan/McGraw-Hill

At Home: Have your child write three sentences describing characters in the story. Have your child use *a* and *an* in his or her descriptions.

Ranita, the Frog Princess
Grade 4/Unit 5

135

Name_____

> • Use *the* with singular nouns that name a particular person, place, or thing.
> • Use *the* before all plural nouns.

Read each sentence. Put one line under each article. Put two lines under the noun that each article points out.

1. The arrow was golden.

2. Félipé thought Ranita was only a frog.

3. Everyone must keep promises, even the children of kings.

4. Pepé feared it would be a long night.

5. Ranita thought Pepé would be the best husband.

6. Félipé ordered Pepé to kiss the frog.

7. Ranita was an unexpected guest.

8. The servants didn't like Félipé much.

9. Vieja Sabia taught both children a lesson in manners.

10. The viceroy argued with his wife.

11. Ranita was actually a Mayan princess.

12. Félipé refused to go to the wedding of Ranita and Pepé.

13. The frog was hopeful for a change.

14. Pepé wore a long cloak.

15. The townspeople did not know the frog.

16. One guest had an overnight bag.

At Home: Have your child write three sentences about the story. Help your child circle the articles in his or her sentences.

© Macmillan/McGraw-Hill

- Use *a* and *an* with singular nouns.
- Use *a* if the next word starts with a consonant sound.
- Use *an* if the next word starts with a vowel sound.
- Use *the* with singular nouns that name a particular person, place, or thing.
- Use *the* before all plural nouns.

Each sentence is missing two articles. Add the articles and write the sentences correctly.

1. Who is boy who lost golden arrow?

   _____

2. Until he went to well, Félipé had never seen talking frog.

   _____

   _____

3. Ranita asked wise woman to turn her into girl again.

   _____

   _____

4. Wife of the viceroy spoiled children.

   _____

5. Cook said, "I added fly to your soup for the frog."

   _____

   _____

6. Adding the fly to soup was excellent idea.

   _____

7. Ranita told woman, "I was selfish child."

   _____

8. Why is boy feeding birds?

   _____

At Home: Ask your child to write a few sentences explaining the message of the story. Remind him or her to use articles correctly.

Name_____

- Use *a* and *an* with singular nouns.
- Use *a* if the next word starts with a consonant sound.
- Use *an* if the next word starts with a vowel sound.
- Use *the* with singular nouns that name a particular person, place, or thing.
- Use *the* before all plural nouns.

Rewrite each sentence in the poster below. Remember to use *a*, *an*, and *the* correctly. Add articles where they are missing.

VICEROY ELEMENTARY SCHOOL ANNOUNCES
A THIRD ANNUAL ARTS AND CRAFTS SHOW!

show will take place on Saturday, March 28
If you have a art project or an craft project to display,
please let fourth-grade art teacher know.
Gift card worth $30 will be awarded
to artist who wins first place.

_____

_____

_____

_____

_____

_____

_____

_____

At Home: Have your child rewrite and decorate his or her poster.

A. Circle the letter before the sentence that uses articles correctly.

1. a. Frog is not allowed to eat from my plate.
b. An frog is not an very clean animal.
c. I would not share my dinner with a frog.

2. a. Mayan emperor's daughter had spell cast on her.
b. Who would have believed she was the Mayan emperor's daughter?
c. A wise woman said manners were important.

3. a. I liked the character of Pepé, the servant.
b. Pepé, the servant, is funny character.
c. Pepé becomes an husband to Ranita.

4. a. What is moral of story?
b. I enjoyed the story.
c. Tell me a important event from the story.

B. Circle the letter before the article that correctly completes each sentence.

5. Which of _____ characters did you like best?
a. a
b. an
c. the

6. There wasn't _____ happy ending for Félipé.
a. a
b. an
c. the

7. Did Ranita _____ frog really sleep in Félipé's bed?
a. a
b. an
c. the

8. Félipé didn't think he had to be nice to Ranita, since she was only _____ animal.
a. a
b. an
c. the

Name_____

- Use *a* and *an* with singular nouns.
- Use *a* if the next word starts with a consonant sound.
- Use *an* if the next word starts with a vowel sound.
- Use *the* with singular nouns that name a particular person, place, or thing.
- Use *the* before all plural nouns.

Read the sentences about what the characters might be saying in the picture below. Rewrite the sentences on the lines below, adding articles where they are needed.

1. FÉLIPÉ: That was not just arrow—it was golden arrow!

_____

2. RANITA: If I rescue arrow, you must make me promise.

_____

3. VIEJA SABIA: Ranita, I will take you to hunting lodge of the viceroy.

_____

_____

4. RANITA: Be sure to set place for me at dinner table!

_____

Name_____

- Add -*er* to most adjectives to compare two people, places, or things.
- Add -*est* to most adjectives to compare more than two.

Read each sentence. Underline the adjective in parentheses that correctly completes the sentence.

1. Have you ever imagined exploring the (deeper, deepest) waters of the ocean?

2. The sun looks (brighter, brightest) on the water than it does on land.

3. The Pacific Ocean looks (clearer, clearest) than the Atlantic Ocean.

4. The blue whale is the (larger, largest) mammal of all.

5. The deep water is (colder, coldest) than the shallow water by the shore.

6. This mussel shell is the (prettier, prettiest) shell I found today.

7. I think scuba divers are the (braver, bravest) of all explorers.

8. It is so much (quieter, quietest) under water than it is on the surface.

9. The colors of this fish are the (stranger, strangest) I have ever seen.

10. Andrea is a (faster, fastest) swimmer than Eric.

11. Which of the waves do you think is (higher, highest)?

12. My towel is (sandier, sandiest) than yours.

13. This fish is (smaller, smallest) than the other one.

14. My shell collection is (better, best) than Ralph's.

15. This rock is the (heavier, heaviest) of them.

16. Andrea can stay afloat (longer, longest) than Cyril can.

© Macmillan/McGraw-Hill

At Home: Have your child write each adjective in parentheses on an index card. With a family member, have your child take turns drawing a card and using the adjectives in sentences of his or her own.

Name_____

- Add -er to most adjectives to compare two people, places, or things.
- Add -est to most adjectives to compare more than two.
- For adjectives ending in e, drop the e before adding -er or -est.
- For adjectives ending in a consonant and y, change the y to i before adding -er or -est.
- For adjectives that have a single vowel before a final consonant, double the final consonant before adding -er or -est.

Rewrite the sentences below, correcting the form or spelling of the underlined adjective.

1. After the sun went down, the air felt <u>chilliest</u> than before.

_____

2. I think fish feel <u>freeer</u> in the ocean than they do in tanks.

_____

3. Dad caught the <u>bigest</u> fish of all.

_____

4. I wonder which ocean is the <u>saltyest</u>.

_____

5. The dolphin is one of the <u>smartiest</u> animals.

_____

6. The water is <u>calmmer</u> than it was yesterday.

_____

7. My clothes are <u>wettest</u> than they were this morning.

_____

8. That shark has the <u>paleest</u> skin I've ever seen.

_____

© Macmillan/McGraw-Hill

At Home: Ask your child to make a chart of five different adjectives to compare by adding -er and -est. Have your child write the three forms of each adjective (such as hot, hotter, hottest).

Name_____

- A proper noun or adjective begins with a capital letter.
- The name of a day, month, or holiday begins with a capital letter.
- Capitalize family names if they refer to specific people.
- Capitalize titles of people before names.

Read the sentences below. Then correct the capitalization mistakes. Rewrite the sentences on the lines provided.

1. The beach was closed after labor day.

_____

2. The dead sea is the lowest place in the world.

_____

3. The north pacific octopus can grow to over 100 pounds.

_____

_____

4. I learned this from dr. stevenson, an expert on ocean life.

_____

_____

5. We are going scuba diving on sunday.

_____

6. We are bringing grandpa along.

_____

7. Jacques cousteau was a famous french undersea explorer.

_____

_____

8. Cousteau was born in june 1910 in france.

_____

At Home: Ask your child to write four sentences that include words that begin in a capital letter.

Rewrite the title and each sentence in the response to literature below. Remember to use –er and –est endings correctly with adjectives. Be sure to capitalize proper nouns, names, and titles.

Response to "exploring the undersea Territory"

I enjoyed reading this article. After learning about undersea explorers, I think that the work they do is strangeer and scaryer than most people's jobs. But it is also more interesting.

One of the braveest explorers of all is sylvia Earle. She was nicknamed "Her deepness" because in 1979 she made the deeper ocean dive any human being had ever made alone. She went on to work as a businesswoman and as a scientist at the National oceanic and Atmospheric Administration.

_____

_____

_____

_____

_____

_____

_____

_____

_____

_____

_____

© Macmillan/McGraw-Hill

 At Home: Have your child write a paragraph about a career that interests him or her. Remind your child to use adjectives ending in -er and -est.

A. Read each sentence. Write yes if the underlined adjective is the correct form or the correct spelling. Write no if it is not the correct form or the correct spelling.

1. Since the bottom of the ocean is the <u>murkyest</u> part, some deep-sea fish have feelers as well as eyes.

   _____

2. The small cookiecutter shark can catch and eat much <u>larger</u> fish.

   _____

3. To me, jellyfish are the <u>scaryest</u> fish.

   _____

4. This clown fish has the <u>brightest</u> colors of all.

   _____

5. It's <u>chillyer</u> in this water than over there.

   _____

6. That is the <u>strangest</u> looking shell of all.

   _____

B. Read each sentence. Use the correct form of the adjective in parentheses. Write it on the line.

7. This lionfish has the (long) _____ spines I have ever seen!

8. Next to the green algae, the coral looked even (red) _____ than before.

9. You will be (safe) _____ if you wear a life preserver.

10. September is one of the (stormy) _____ months.

11. This fish tastes (salty) _____ than the other one.

12. You look (pale) _____ than I do.

Name

- Add -*er* to most adjectives to compare two people, places, or things.
- Add -*est* to most adjectives to compare more than two.
- For adjectives ending in *e*, drop the *e* before adding -*er* or -*est*.
- For adjectives ending in a consonant and *y*, change the *y* to *i* before adding -*er* or -*est*.
- For adjectives that have a single vowel before a final consonant, double the final consonant before adding -*er* or -*est*.

Mechanics

- Proper adjectives are formed from proper nouns.
- A proper adjective or proper noun begins with a capital letter.

Read the sentences below. Look for mistakes in how adjectives are formed and how words are capitalized. Rewrite the sentences correctly.

1. The Great barrier Reef near australia is the largeest reef that living creatures have built.

_____

2. The sea turtles of australia are the cuter turtles I have ever seen.

_____

3. The red bass is the olddest fish on the great barrier reef.

_____

4. Aunt carol said most clams are much tinyer than the giant clam.

_____

Name_____

> • For long adjectives, use *more* and *most* to compare people, places, or things.
> • Use *more* to compare two people, places, or things.
> • Use *most* to compare more than two.

Write *more* or *most* to complete each sentence correctly.

1. Your lemon cake is the _____ delicious dessert of all.

2. Uncle Romie had an even _____ enormous belly than my father.

3. He made the _____ interesting collage I have ever seen.

4. New York City is _____ exciting than my hometown.

5. But for me, North Carolina will always be the _____ comfortable place in the world.

6. Uncle Romie's studio was the _____ glorious mess I had ever seen!

7. I thought my birthday would be _____ pleasant if Aunt Nanette were there.

8. This birthday turned out to be the _____ special birthday ever.

9. Uncle Romie was _____ familiar with New York baseball teams than I was.

10. This summer vacation was _____ enjoyable than last year's vacation.

11. Could this get _____ exciting than yesterday?

12. This is the _____ fun I've ever had.

© Macmillan/McGraw-Hill

At Home: Ask your child to write four sentences of his or her own, using adjectives from the above sentences. Have your child use *more* and *most* in their sentences.

Me and Uncle Romie

147

Grade 4/Unit 5

Name

> - For long adjectives, use *more* and *most* to compare people, places, or things.
> - Use *more* to compare two people, places, or things.
> - Use *most* to compare more than two.
> - When you use *more* or *most*, do not use the ending *-er* or *-est*.

Rewrite each sentence. Use the correct form of the adjective.

1. Harlem is the more excitingest place I've ever been.

_____

2. The sounds of the traffic outside made me feel more awaker than at home.

_____

_____

3. At first, Aunt Nanette seemed more caringer than Uncle Romie.

_____

4. My visit to my grandparents' house is the most peacefulest time I can remember.

_____

_____

5. My aunt and uncle are most importanter to me than they used to be.

_____

_____

6. Uncle Romie is the most artisticest person I know.

_____

7. I was more carefuller with this collage than I usually am.

_____

8. My mother makes the more excellentest pepper jelly I have ever tasted.

_____

_____

At Home: Encourage your child to recall his or her favorite place. Have your child describe the place in oral sentences using *-er*, *-est*, *more*, and *most*.

Name_____

- When you start a sentence with an introductory word that is not part of the complete subject or predicate, follow it with a comma.
- Some common introductory words are *yes*, *no*, and *well*.
- When the sentence begins by addressing someone by name, use a comma after the name.

Rewrite the sentences below correctly. Use a comma after any introductory word or name.

1. B. J. the train is coming now.

_____

2. Well New York will certainly be different from North Carolina.

_____

3. Uncle Romie did you make that project?

_____

4. Yes I worked on it for months.

_____

5. James I'm pleased to meet you.

_____

6. Aunt Nanette I will miss you tomorrow.

_____

7. No I am sorry, but I cannot come to your party.

_____

8. Mama I missed you so much.

_____

9. Yes I brought you a jar of pepper jelly.

_____

10. No we did not expect to have twins.

_____

© Macmillan/McGraw-Hill

At Home: Ask your child to write a few sentences of dialogue for the characters in the story. Have your child start the sentences with names or expressions such as *yes*, *no*, and *well*.

Name _____

- For long adjectives, use *more* and *most* to compare people, places, or things.
- Use *more* to compare two people, places, or things.
- Use *most* to compare more than two.

Rewrite each sentence in the introduction speech below. Remember to use *more* and *most* correctly with adjectives. Use a comma after an introductory word used at the beginning of a sentence. Use a comma when the first word in the sentence addresses someone by name.

Class I would like to introduce my Uncle Romie to you. I met him last summer when I visited New York. He is the most creativest, most imaginativest person I know! His work is more unusualer and more powerfuler than any painting in a museum. Is he a painter? Is he a photographer? Is he a writer? No he's all of those at once. He puts paint, pictures, newspapers, magazines, and other things together to make the most amazing collages. His collage of Harlem is the more joyfulest picture I've ever seen. Yes I have also started making collages, just like Uncle Romie.

_____

_____

_____

_____

_____

_____

_____

_____

At Home: Have your child read sentences from the corrected speech aloud.

Name_____

**A. In each sentence, find the adjective that compares.
Circle your answer.**

1. My sister is more musical than my brother is.
   a. sister
   b. more musical
   c. musical than
   d. brother is

2. New York City is one of the most popular of all cities to visit.
   a. New York
   b. the most
   c. most popular
   d. all cities

3. My Aunt Nanette is the most generous person I know.
   a. most generous
   b. Aunt Nanette
   c. generous person
   d. I know

**B. Choose the correct adjective to complete each sentence.
Circle your answer.**

4. My sister was _____ about my trip than my brother was.
   a. curious
   b. curiouser
   c. more curious
   d. most curious

5. John is the _____ of all three children.
   a. responsible
   b. responsiblest
   c. more responsible
   d. most responsible

6. That is the _____ idea I ever heard.
   a. original
   b. originalest
   c. more original
   d. most original

Name_____

Read the sentences below. Look for mistakes in adjectives that compare. Rewrite the sentences correctly. Then read them aloud.

1. Of all the students in our class, I was the eagerest to visit the art museum.

_____

_____

2. The rooms on the first floor have old-fashioneder paintings than the rooms on the second floor.

_____

_____

3. The paintings on the third floor are the modernest of all.

_____

_____

4. We decided packing a lunch would be economicaler than buying one.

_____

_____

© Macmillan/McGraw-Hill

Name

- Use *better* to compare two people, places, or things.
- Use *best* to compare more than two.

Write *better* or *best* to complete each sentence correctly.

1. The Black Hills Wild Horse Sanctuary is one of the _____ places to see wild horses.

2. My friend thinks horses are _____ companions than dogs.

3. Dayton Hyde thinks that running free is _____ for horses than being stuck in one place.

4. He thought the _____ choice would be to fence the horses in at first.

5. Because he grew up on a ranch, Dayton understands horses _____ than most of us do.

6. Life was _____ for most wild horses in the 1800s than it was in the 1900s.

7. Conditions were _____ for population growth after a 1971 law outlawed the capture of wild horses.

8. Dayton Hyde created the _____ place for wild horses to run free.

9. Horse ranches are the _____ places to learn to ride.

10. His horse is _____ at racing than mine is.

11. This is the _____ spot for a horse to drink.

12. Is it _____ to ride sidesaddle or western style?

At Home: Have your child read an article in a newspaper or magazine and circle each use of *better* or *best*.

Name _____

- Use *worse* to compare two people, places, or things.
- Use *worst* to compare more than two.

Write *worse* or *worst* to complete each sentence correctly.

1. The invention of barbed-wire fences made life _____ for wild horses than before.

2. During the _____ period, the population of horses fell below 17,000.

3. Hunger and thirst were the _____ threats to horses.

4. Seeing wild horses in fenced feedlots made Dayton Hyde feel _____ than he had for a long time.

5. The ranch was no _____ than the feedlot.

6. The thought of the horses breaking down the fence was Dayton's _____ fear.

7. Conditions were _____ for horses after more land was settled.

8. The cold felt _____ for the cowboys than it did for the horses.

9. This is the _____ time to ride a horse.

10. My saddle sore is no _____ than yours, I suppose.

11. That's not the _____ riding I've ever seen.

12. That trail is much _____ than this trail.

At Home: Ask your child and a family member to write four sentences, two with *worse* and two with *worst*.

© Macmillan/McGraw-Hill

Name_____

- Use *better* to compare two people, places, or things.
- Use *best* to compare more than two.
- Use *worse* to compare two people, places, or things.
- Use *worst* to compare more than two.
- Do not use *more*, *most*, *-er*, or *-est* with *better*, *best*, *worse*, or *worst*.

Read the sentences below. Look for comparisons that use forms of *good* and *bad* incorrectly. Rewrite the sentences correctly.

1. Angie is best at taking care of horses than I am.

_____

2. Justin is the most best rider I know.

_____

3. The drought grew worser when it didn't rain all summer.

_____

_____

4. That was the most worst day he ever had.

_____

5. Her limp is getting badder.

_____

6. What food is bestest for horses?

_____

7. Their health will be more betterer if you give them vitamins.

_____

8. Troublemaker's behavior was the worstest of all the horses.

_____

_____

At Home: Have your child write three sentences about the story, using the forms of *good* and *bad* to make comparisons.

Name_____

Rewrite each sentence in the scientific observation below. Remember to use forms of *good* and *bad* correctly.

QUESTION: What is the bestest way to approach a horse?
OBSERVATIONS: Calm horses have relaxed muscles, heads, and necks. Frightened horses may raise their heads and tense their muscles. Flattened ears are one of the most worst signs of fear.

   Alan and Maria approached the horse named Bertha. The trainer, Marcos, was with them. (It is always goodest to have adults present for safety.) When Alan walked loudly toward Bertha from behind, her signs of fear grew worser. When Maria walked slowly and quietly toward Bertha from the left front side, Bertha stayed more calmer. She seemed to like this approach much more better. CONCLUSION: Approaching a horse from the front or side is gooder than approaching from behind.

_____

_____

_____

_____

_____

_____

_____

_____

_____

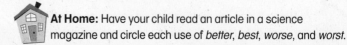
At Home: Have your child read an article in a science magazine and circle each use of *better*, *best*, *worse*, and *worst*.

Name_____

A. Read each sentence. Write *yes* if the underlined adjective is the correct form of *good*. Write *no* if it is not correct.

1. I think the Black Hills Sanctuary would be the <u>better</u> place in the world to work. _____

2. This stall is <u>better</u> than that one. _____

3. Summer is the <u>best</u> of all seasons. _____

4. I remember this story the <u>better</u> of all. _____

5. Yuskeya is a <u>best</u> runner than Funny Face is. _____

6. This horse farm is the <u>better</u> of them. _____

7. My saddle is <u>better</u> than yours. _____

8. This view is <u>best</u> than the other one. _____

B. Read each sentence. Decide if the missing adjective is *worse* or *worst*. Write it on the line.

9. Chocolate is one of the _____ foods you could give to pets.

10. Chocolate is much _____ for animals than it is for humans.

11. My horse felt _____ last week than he does this week.

12. This is the _____ fence I have seen in my life.

13. Last year's weather was bad, but this year's weather is _____.

14. This trail is the _____ one I've seen.

15. Yuskeya's left hoof is in _____ shape than the others.

16. My feet feel the _____ in these awful boots.

Name_____

- Use *better* to compare two people, places, or things.
- Use *best* to compare more than two.
- Use *worse* to compare two people, places, or things.
- Use *worst* to compare more than two.

Mechanics

- Do not use *more*, *most*, *-er*, or *-est* with *better*, *best*, *worse*, or *worst*.

Read the sentences about the picture. Correct the adjectives that are not written correctly.

1. What is the bestest place for animals to live?

_____

2. Would it be best for a horse to live on a farm or to run wild?

_____

_____

3. What would be the worse part of living on a farm?

_____

4. What might make running wild the worst of the two choices?

_____

_____

© Macmillan/McGraw-Hill

Name_____

Read each passage and look at the underlined sentences. Is there a mistake? If there is, how do you correct it? Circle your answer.

(1) My dog Brownie is a german shepherd. He looks strong and a little scary. (2) However, Brownie is actually very gentle. Anyone is safe with him.

1. **A.** Add capitalization.
   B. Add punctuation.
   C. Use a better adjective.
   D. No mistake.

2. **E.** Add capitalization.
   F. Add punctuation.
   G. Use a better adjective.
   H. No mistake.

(3) Félipé, the spanish viceroy's son, was rude to Ranita. He thought she was only a frog. (4) He didn't know a woman had put a spell on her. She was really an emperor's daughter.

3. **A.** Add capitalization.
   B. Add punctuation.
   C. Change the article.
   D. No mistake.

4. **E.** Add capitalization.
   F. Add punctuation.
   G. Change the article.
   H. No mistake.

Name_____

(5) I think collages are hard to make than paintings. You need to find all sorts of different materials to use. Sometimes finding the right materials is a matter of luck. (6) To me, that's also what makes collages interesting than paintings.

5. A. Adjective needs an ending.
   B. Adjective needs *more*.
   C. Adjective needs *most*.
   D. No mistake.

6. E. Adjective needs an ending.
   F. Adjective needs *more*.
   G. Adjective needs *most*.
   H. No mistake.

Animals face many challenges living in the wild. (7) Still, some animals like living in the wild best than living as pets or on a farm. For example, dogs and cats like living as pets in people's homes. (8) But wild horses seem to think that's much worse than dogs and cats do.

7. A. Add punctuation.
   B. Change use of *better* or *best*.
   C. Change use of *worse* or *worst*.
   D. No mistake.

8. E. Add punctuation.
   F. Change use of *better* or *best*.
   G. Change use of *worse* or *worst*.
   H. No mistake.

- **Adjectives** and **adverbs** should not be confused.
- An **adjective** describes nouns. It gives information about a *person*, *place*, or *thing*.
- An **adverb** tells more about the verb, such as *how*, *when*, and *where* an action takes place.

Read each sentence and look at the underlined word. Then tell if the word is an adjective or an adverb.

1. In 1848, many people <u>quickly</u> moved to California in search of gold.

   _____

2. The forty-niners hoped to become <u>rich</u> men. _____

3. I like to read <u>interesting</u> stories about the California Gold Rush.

   _____

4. Show your father the treasure map that you found <u>yesterday</u>.

   _____

5. The miner dug <u>deeply</u> into the hole to see if there was gold inside.

   _____

6. I do not think that what you found in the river is <u>real</u> gold.

   _____

7. On our field trip to the gold mine, our guide led us through a <u>dark</u> tunnel.

   _____

8. Matt and Eric were standing by a <u>muddy</u> road. _____

9. Raven <u>always</u> wanted to travel back in time to see how her

   neighborhood used to look. _____

10. They <u>eagerly</u> waited to join the wagon train to California.

   _____

At Home: Have your child rewrite three of the above sentences, replacing the underlined adjective or adverb with another of his or her choosing.

Name _____

> • An **adverb** is a word that tells more about a verb.
> • Some adverbs tell *how* an action takes place.
> • Some adverbs tell *when* an action takes place.
> • Some adverbs tell *where* an action takes place.

Underline the adverb in each sentence. Then write if the adverb tells *how*, *when*, or *where* the action takes place.

1. My mother and I went to the library together for information about our ancestors. _____

2. Many Native Americans lived freely on this land. _____

3. Tomorrow we will visit our local museum of natural history.

   _____

4. Were they traveling far in search of gold? _____

5. Did James Marshall first find gold at Sutter's Mill? _____

6. John Sutter, Jr. built a new city nearby along the Sacramento River.

   _____

7. We patiently sifted the sand for gold. _____

8. Our uncle examined the rock carefully. _____

9. He carelessly threw the stone back in the water. _____

10. That greedy miner looked at them suspiciously. _____

11. We quickly ran down the path. _____

12. We then found the gold. _____

At Home: Have your child write three sentences, one with a word that tells *how*, one with a word that tells *when*, and one with a word that tells *where*.

- *Good* is an adjective and is used to describe nouns.
- *Well* is an adverb that tells *how* about a verb.
- Do not confuse the adjective *good* with the adverb *well*.
- Use *well* as an adjective when you refer to someone's health.

Complete each sentence by writing the word *good* or *well* on the line.

1. Today our team did _____ in the class treasure-hunt game.

2. Our teacher hid the treasure pieces so _____ that they were very hard to find.

3. The other team also did _____, but we found the pieces faster than they did.

4. Though I didn't feel _____, I helped find the last, hidden treasure piece.

5. It was a _____ experience to win the game for a second year.

6. This river is a _____ place to look for gold pieces.

7. Grandfather, would it be a _____ idea to look for gold in the river?

8. If we pan for gold all day and night, we should do _____.

9. We can have a _____ time swimming in the water if we do not find anything.

10. Is your father feeling _____ enough to come with us?

© Macmillan/McGraw-Hill

At Home: Have your child write two sentences that tell things that are *good* and two sentences that tell something that he or she did *well*.

The Gold Rush Game • Grade 4/Unit 6 (163)

- An **adverb** is a word that tells more about a verb.
- Some adverbs tell *how* an action takes place.
- Most adverbs that tell *how* end in *-ly*. They are formed by adding *-ly* to an adjective.

Read the magazine article below and circle the six incorrect adverbs. Then write the words correctly on the lines below.

When the gold miners of 1849 were looking for gold, they frequent found shiny stones in their pans. However, not all were true gold. Fool's gold, also called pyrite, is a stone that some miners mistaken confused with the real thing. What if you ever find a rock that looks like gold? These three ways can quick help you find out if it is real gold or fool's gold.

First, look careful at the color. Both are shiny and yellow-colored, but real gold also has a silver tone. The color of fool's gold is more like brass. Next, look at the shape. Fool's gold usual forms cubes and larger shapes. Real gold comes in chunks, flakes, or sheets. Last, brisk rub it against another hard object and smell it. Gold has no smell, but fool's gold will smell a little like rotten eggs. Maybe that's why they call it *fool's* gold!

1. _____ 3. _____ 5. _____

2. _____ 4. _____ 6. _____

Rewrite the above article with the correct adverbs on the lines provided.

_____

_____

_____

_____

_____

At Home: Have your child tell you three things that he or she did skillfully. Have him or her use the word *skillfully* in the response.

Read each sentence. Then using the clue in the parentheses, circle the letter of the correct adverb that completes each sentence.

1. After gold was discovered at Sutter's Mill, many people moved _____. (where?)

   a. there

   b. well

   c. briefly

   d. quietly

2. Her grandfather traveled _____ to California to search for gold. (how?)

   a. today

   b. outside

   c. bravely

   d. ahead

3. Her grandfather shouted _____ when he saw a piece of gold in the river. (how?)

   a. well

   b. next

   c. around

   d. gleefully

4. His shouting was so loud, it could be heard near and _____. (where?)

   a. far

   b. first

   c. soon

   d. silent

5. People _____ came from everywhere to see why her grandfather was shouting. (when?)

   a. forcefully

   b. wisely

   c. eagerly

   d. quickly

6. _____ he realized that it was just a piece of fool's gold. (when?)

   a. Unhappily

   b. Excitedly

   c. Then

   d. Nearly

Name_____

- An **adverb** is a word that tells more about a verb.
- Some adverbs tell *how* an action takes place.
- Most adverbs that tell *how* end in *-ly*. They are formed by adding *-ly* to an adjective.

Mechanics

- *Good* is an adjective and is used to describe nouns.
- *Well* is an adverb that tells *how* about a verb.
- Use *well* as an adjective when you refer to someone's health.
- Do not confuse the adjective *good* with the adverb *well*.

Read each sentence below. Then write the correct form of the underlined word on the line.

1. The river <u>rapid</u> washes mud and sand into their pans. _____

2. They <u>brief</u> stop to check if any gold is inside. _____

3. Looking for gold, they <u>cautious</u> swirl the pans around. _____

4. The men must hold their pans <u>careful</u> so they do not fall into the water.

_____

5. They talked <u>hopeful</u> about finding many pieces of gold. _____

Name_____

- An **adverb** can compare two or more actions.
- Add -*er* to short adverbs to compare two actions.
- Add -*est* to short adverbs to compare more than two actions.

Add -*er* or -*est* to each boldfaced adverb to complete the sentences below. Remember to drop the final e or change *y* to *i* when necessary before adding -*er* or -*est*.

1. **fast**   In the country, I walk the _____ of all.

2. **slow**   When I get tired, I move _____ than my brother.

3. **hard**   These builders worked _____ than the others to finish on time.

4. **high**   We will climb _____ than the first team to reach the top of the hill.

5. **low**   Birds fly _____ over the city than they do here.

6. **tall**   The mountains here rise _____ than city buildings.

7. **close**   We live _____ to the river than you do.

8. **late**   We sleep _____ in the city than we do here.

9. **early**   We rise _____ in the mountains than in the city.

10. **long**   The sunsets here last _____ of all.

At Home: Have your child rewrite three of the above sentences, replacing the underlined word with another one.

The Cricket in Times Square   167
Grade 4/Unit 6

- Use *more* or *most* to form comparisons with adverbs that end in *-ly* or with longer adverbs.
- Use *more* to compare two actions.
- Use *most* to compare more than two actions.
- When you use *more* or *most*, do not use the ending *-er* or *-est*.

Use *more* or *most* with the underlined adverb in each first sentence to complete the two sentences that follow.

1. The train that Chester was on shook <u>harshly</u> as it moved on the track.

   The second train shook _____ every now and then.

   But the subway car shook _____ of all.

2. Chester <u>furiously</u> tried to escape from the picnic basket.

   He tried _____ as the train rattled and shook.

   Chester tried the _____ of all when they finally reached New York.

3. Harry Cat <u>speedily</u> jumped toward Chester and Tucker Mouse.

   Chester jumped the _____ of all into the matchbox.

   Chester jumped _____ than Harry Cat.

4. Chester chirps <u>sweetly</u> when he is excited.

   Chester chirps _____ when he is scared.

   But Chester chirps the _____ when he is happy.

5. Chester moves <u>hastily</u> through the drain pipe.

   Harry Cat moves _____ through the drain pipe.

   But Tucker moves the _____ of all through the drain pipe.

At Home: Have your child look in magazine articles to find examples of comparative adverbs formed with *more* or *most*.

Name_____

> - An **adverb** can compare two or more actions.
> - Add *-er* to short adverbs to compare two actions.
> - Add *-est* to short adverbs to compare more than two actions.
> - Use *more* or *most* to form comparisons with adverbs that end in *-ly* or with longer adverbs.
> - Use *more* to compare two actions.
> - Use *most* to compare more than two actions.
> - When you use *more* or *most*, do not use the ending *-er* or *-est*.

Add *more* or *most* to the beginning of each boldfaced adverb to complete the sentences below.

1. **easily**   Tucker Mouse moves through the city

_____ than Chester.

2. **clumsily**   Of the three friends, Chester runs the

_____ through Times Square.

3. **terribly**   Times Square upset Chester _____ than he had imagined.

4. **kindly**   Harry Cat treats mice and crickets _____ than other cats do.

5. **politely**   City cats behave _____ than country cats.

6. **speedily**   Chester thought that Harry ran the _____ of all.

7. **widely**   Chester opened his eyes _____ as he got used to the lights.

8. **dazzlingly**   Of all the lights in the sky, there was one star that shone

the _____.

At Home: Have your child write three sentences about a trip that include examples of words that compare with *more* or *most*.

The Cricket in Times Square

169

Grade 4/Unit 6

© Macmillan/McGraw-Hill

Read the magazine article below and circle the six incorrect adverbs.

In a nest near school, a baby bird chirped loud than a grown bird. It sad seems that the bird got lost when its family went south. The bird was not used to the cold weather, so it hid inside the nest. Then a young boy and his uncle heard it chirping frantic in the tree.

They took the baby bird to the animal hospital. The doctor there kind offered to take the bird to the zoo. At the zoo, the workers are feeding it more careful. It is feeling much better now. As soon as it gets completely well, the zoo will send it south to be with other birds. It will live safe in a warm climate than a cold one.

Rewrite the above article with the correct adverbs on the lines below.

_____

_____

_____

_____

_____

_____

_____

_____

_____

_____

At Home: Have your child write about a sick animal that he or she has helped nurse back to health.

A. For each of the adverbs below, write the form you would use to compare two things. Then choose one of the adverbs you formed and use it in a sentence.

1. close _____

2. curiously _____

3. carefully _____

4. soon _____

5. gloomily _____

6. tall _____

7. loudly _____

8. _____

_____

B. For each of the following adverbs, write the form you would use to compare more than two things. Then choose one of the adverbs you formed and use it in a sentence.

9. graciously _____

10. playfully _____

11. straight _____

12. heavily _____

13. hard _____

14. sweetly _____

15. sadly _____

16. _____

_____

Name_____

- Add *-er* to short adverbs to compare two actions.
- Add *-est* to short adverbs to compare more than two actions.
- Use *more* to compare two actions with longer adverbs.
- Use *most* to compare more than two actions with longer adverbs.

Add comparative adverbs to complete the sentences below.

1. The trains run _____ on weekends than during the week.

2. Tucker got hungry _____ than the others.

3. Tucker told his story _____ when Chester was listening.

4. Subway trains screech _____ than regular trains.

5. Of the three friends, Tucker moved _____ through the drain pipe.

6. He unpacked the picnic basket _____ than Chester.

7. Tucker shook his head _____ than Chester.

8. On New Year's Eve, the city lights shine _____ than on other nights.

9. Harry Cat grew _____ than the rest of them.

10. Now people helped him _____ than they had before.

11. Some acted _____ than others.

12. The siren blared _____ of all.

Name_____

> • A **negative** is a word that means "no," such as *not*, *never*, *nobody*, *nowhere*, and contractions with *n't*.
> • Do not use two negatives in the same sentence.
> • You can fix a sentence with two negatives by removing one.

Correct each sentence by removing one of the negatives. Then rewrite the sentence.

1. Imagine if we didn't never know about dinosaurs.

_____

2. What if there wasn't no place you could go to see their bones?

_____

_____

3. Maybe you never thought nothing about it.

_____

4. A long time ago, people weren't never interested in studying dinosaurs.

_____

_____

5. There wasn't no effort made to keep bones and other items that were found.

_____

_____

6. We didn't never have a way to know how these animals lived.

_____

7. There weren't never museums like there are today.

_____

8. Years ago, there wasn't no one who wanted to search for dinosaurs.

_____

_____

© Macmillan/McGraw-Hill

At Home: Have your child listen carefully to TV shows for examples of two negatives like the ones in this lesson.

Meet a Bone-ified Explorer

173

Name_____

- You can correct a sentence with two negatives by changing one negative to a positive word.

  no—any   nothing—anything   no one—anyone

  never—ever   nobody—anybody   nowhere—anywhere

Correct these sentences by changing one negative word to a positive word.

1. Hakeem never wanted nothing to do with science.

_____

2. He didn't like to be nowhere near dirt and bones.

_____

3. His teacher thought he wouldn't never pass her class.

_____

4. There wasn't nobody who disliked science more than he did.

_____

_____

5. Hakeem hadn't never seen anything like that piece of amber.

_____

_____

6. Now there isn't no class more fun than science.

_____

7. Hakeem isn't never late for class anymore.

_____

8. There isn't no better way to thank her for what she did.

_____

_____

© Macmillan/McGraw-Hill

At Home: Ask your child to write a short paragraph about a trip to a natural history museum or exhibit. Encourage your child to check his or her work for double negatives.

Name _____

- Do not use two negatives in the same sentence.
- You can fix a sentence with two negatives by removing one.
- You can correct a sentence with two negatives by changing one negative to a positive word.

Rewrite each sentence below by dropping a negative or changing one negative to a positive word.

1. I haven't found nothing in this area yet.

_____

2. Our team didn't waste no time finding the skeleton.

_____

3. Don't never go out in the bright sun without putting on a hat.

_____

_____

4. There isn't no place to find dinosaur bones here.

_____

_____

5. I wouldn't never want to see a dinosaur in real life.

_____

6. Doesn't no one know about the oldest fossil ever found?

_____

_____

7. The team couldn't find the sunken ship nowhere.

_____

8. Iris didn't put no labels on the stones she found.

_____

At Home: Have your child review the strategies he or she used to correct the sentences on this page. Then have him or her try to correct each sentence by using another possible strategy.

Meet a Bone-ified Explorer **175**
Grade 4/Unit 6

Name_____

Read the personal essay below. Underline the sentences that contain two negatives.

The New Kid in Class

Last month, I started going to a new school. I didn't know nobody at this school. At first, I thought there wasn't no way I would be comfortable here.

The teacher introduced me to the class. I had to tell them a little about myself. Everyone was laughing at me. I didn't have no idea what to say. I told the class about how I'd seen a real bear far off in the woods.

Instead of laughing at me, the students were all listening to me. They asked me lots of questions. I still don't know if I'll get used to this new school, but my first day didn't turn out so bad.

Rewrite the above personal essay, correcting the sentences that contain two negatives.

_____

_____

_____

_____

_____

_____

_____

_____

_____

_____

At Home: Invite your child to write two "rules" for making a new child feel welcome in a class or on a team.

A. Each numbered sentence contains two negatives. Circle the answer choice that best revises it.

1. Sue can't think of nothing more exciting than finding fossils.
   a. Sue can think of anything more exciting than finding fossils.
   b. Sue can't not think of anything more exciting than finding fossils.
   c. Sue can't think of anything more exciting than finding fossils.
   d. Sue can think of nothing no more exciting than finding fossils.

2. No one nowhere had found a dinosaur smaller than this one.
   a. No one never had found a dinosaur smaller than this one.
   b. No one anywhere had found a dinosaur smaller than this one.
   c. Not no one anywhere had found a dinosaur smaller than this one.
   d. Nobody nowhere had found a dinosaur smaller than this one.

3. Isn't amber not always a golden color?
   a. Isn't any amber always a golden color?
   b. Is amber never no golden color?
   c. Is amber always no golden color?
   d. Isn't amber always a golden color?

4. That sunken ship isn't nowhere near here.
   a. That sunken ship is anywhere near here.
   b. That sunken ship isn't not nowhere near here.
   c. That sunken ship isn't nowhere ever near here.
   d. That sunken ship is nowhere near here.

5. Scientists didn't have no equipment to explore the tops of rainforest trees.
   a. Scientists didn't have any equipment to explore the tops of rainforest trees.
   b. Scientists did have no equipment to explore the tops of rainforest trees.
   c. Scientists didn't never have equipment to explore the tops of rainforest trees.
   d. Scientists did have equipment to not explore the tops of rainforest trees.

6. Nobody never knew that the lost city was right under them.
   a. Nobody not never knew that the lost city was right under them.
   b. Nobody didn't never know that the lost city was right under them.
   c. Nobody ever knew that the lost city was right under them.
   d. No one never knew that the lost city was right under them.

Name_____

Correct the sentences, remembering the rules, to make them describe the pictures.

1. Kim hadn't never believed dinosaurs could be so huge.

_____

_____

2. There weren't no animals bigger than this.

_____

3. Dad says that no one had never found a dinosaur this big before.

_____

_____

4. Tavon didn't find nothing in the ground today.

_____

5. He couldn't never find anything interesting in his backyard.

_____

_____

© Macmillan/McGraw-Hill

Name_____

- A **preposition** comes before a noun or pronoun and relates that noun or pronoun to another word in a sentence.
- Common prepositions are *about, above, across, after, around, at, behind, down, for, from, in, near, of, on, over, to, under,* and *with*.

Complete each sentence by adding a preposition.

1. Papa brought home a little flying machine _____ the kids.

2. Mama never complained _____ Orv and Will's messes.

3. The two older brothers did not agree _____ Orv and Will's ideas.

4. Only the family knew _____ Orv and Will's plans.

5. There was no place _____ their home where they could fly a plane.

6. Flying _____ Kitty Hawk grounds was a good idea.

7. Orv and Will's plane flew _____ the ground.

8. Katherine took her first ride almost six years _____ the first flight.

9. Riding _____ an early plane was dangerous.

10. I like the wind _____ my hair.

11. The plane landed _____ the field.

12. He left the plans _____ the floor.

At Home: Have your child select a paragraph from *My Brothers' Flying Machine* and look for sentences that contain the prepositions listed above.

My Brothers' Flying Machine **179**
Grade 4/Unit 6

Name_____

- A **prepositional phrase** is a group of words that begins with a preposition and ends with a noun or pronoun.

Underline the prepositional phrases in the following sentences.

1. When they finished their first plane, Orv and Katherine went on a camping trip.

2. Will flew the plane over a group of boys.

3. Katherine helped her brothers by managing their shop.

4. In their letters, they told her everything they were doing.

5. Will said that Kitty Hawk was a safe place for practice.

6. The world had never before seen a craft fly in the air.

7. First, they controlled their aircraft from the ground.

8. They came home to Dayton with a new idea.

9. Orv and Will worked from day to night.

10. They had their friend Charlie build an engine for their new aircraft.

11. "It could not be assembled in our shop."

12. The first flight of the *Flyer* was made by Will.

13. They wrote ideas on paper.

14. The brothers rode into town.

15. People flocked to the field.

16. The flights were printed in the newspapers.

At Home: Ask you child to write three sentences that contain the prepositional phrase "in the air." Encourage your child to make the sentences humorous.

Name

- Use quotation marks at the beginning and end of a person's exact words.
- Begin a quotation with a capital letter.
- Begin a new paragraph each time a new person speaks.

Rewrite this passage correctly. Add quotation marks and capital letters where needed. Begin new paragraphs whenever necessary.

what are you making, Rashid? I'm making a paper airplane, Papa, but I can't get it to fly, said Rashid. it looks good, but maybe you need to make the wings longer, his father answered. okay, Papa, what else? well, your grandmother used to open a little space in the middle of the plane for air to travel through. now, let's see what happens. Hey, it's flying, Papa! yelled Rashid.

_____

_____

_____

_____

_____

_____

_____

_____

At Home: Ask your child to write down a short conversation between him or her and a family member, adding _he said_ and _she said_ at appropriate points.

Read the interview below. Then rewrite each line by switching the preposition in each underlined phrase with the correct one from another sentence.

1. "Captain Reilly, what do you like most <u>inside exploring space</u>?"

   _____

   _____

2. "I like the feeling that I am <u>about another world</u>. It's exciting."

   _____

   _____

3. "What is your job <u>to the space shuttle</u>?"

   _____

4. "I help the other crewmembers with repairs <u>from the ship</u>."

   _____

   _____

5. "What can kids learn <u>for exploring space</u>?"

   _____

6. "Exploring space can help kids <u>above their science and math classes</u>."

   _____

   _____

7. "Do you have any advice <u>in our audience</u>?"

   _____

8. "Yes. There is a whole world <u>with you, kids</u>. Discover it!"

   _____

   _____

At Home: Ask your child to read a passage in a favorite book, leaving out all the prepositional phrases he or she can find in it. Then discuss how useful those missing phrases actually are.

© Macmillan/McGraw-Hill

Name_____

A. Complete each sentence below by writing the missing preposition.

1. Papa tossed the flying machine _____ the air.

2. Reuchlin and Lorin looked down _____ Orv and Will's new hobby.

3. Will sold kites to the other kids _____ school.

4. Orv and Will built their first craft _____ the bicycle shop.

5. However, the *Flyer* was so big, they had to build it _____ the shop.

6. They tacked their plans _____ the wall.

7. He hopped _____ the plane's body.

B. Underline the prepositional phrase in each of the sentences below.

8 Orv and Will took weeks preparing for their first flight.

9. On December 14, 1903, the *Flyer* rattled down the track.

10. Will flew the aircraft fifteen feet above ground.

11. Orv watched the flight from the ground below.

12. One day, human beings would fly around the world.

13. They kept the plans in a safe place.

14. The crowd stood in place.

15. The plane stayed above the ground.

- A **preposition** comes before a noun or pronoun and relates that noun or pronoun to another word in a sentence.
- A **prepositional phrase** is a group of words that begins with a preposition and ends with a noun or pronoun.

Mechanics

- Begin the greeting and closing in a letter with a capital letter.
- Use a comma after the greeting and the closing in a letter.
- Use a comma between the names of a city and a state.
- Use a comma between the day and year in a date.

Add capital letters, commas, and prepositions to correct and complete this letter.

6848 Marigold Drive

Columbus Ohio 43221

December 14 2006

dear Grandpa

    Thank you _____ the cookies. How did you shape them _____ airplanes? I told all my friends how my great-great-grandma saw the Wright Brothers fly. They didn't believe me, but I know it's the truth. I hope you come visit us soon. Maybe Spot can come _____ you.

love

Tolu

Name_____

> • Two sentences can be combined by adding a **prepositional phrase** to one sentence.

Combine the pairs of sentences below by using the prepositional phrase from the second sentence. Then underline the prepositional phrase.

1. Today our class went bird-watching. We were at the park.

_____

2. There were many birds to see. They were in the trees.

_____

3. I could see a baby bird. It was inside a small nest.

_____

4. The baby bird was crying. It was crying with its mouth open.

_____

5. There was a mother bird. She was above the baby.

_____

6. The mother fed the baby. She fed the baby by giving her a worm.

_____

7. The baby bird hid. She hid inside the nest.

_____

8. The mother bird flew across. She flew to another tree.

_____

At Home: Ask your child to write four more sentences telling about something he or she might see at the park. Encourage your child to combine them with a prepositional phrase.

The Life and Times of the Ant   **185**
Grade 4/Unit 6

Name_____

> • Two sentences can be combined by adding a **prepositional
> phrase** to one sentence.

**Rewrite the sentences below, using the prepositional phrase to
combine them into one sentence.**

1. Ants make their anthills by digging. They dig through dirt.

_____

2. Ants scoop dirt. They scoop with their jaws.

_____

3. Ants live like people. They live in social communities.

_____

4. Most ants live and work together. They live under the ground.

_____

5. The queen ant lays eggs. She does this inside the hive.

_____

6. Worker ants protect the queen. They protect her from harm.

_____

7. Male ants die. They die after mating with the queen.

_____

8. Ant eggs develop into adult ants. They develop after three months.

_____

© Macmillan/McGraw-Hill

At Home: Ask your child to write two short sentences about
ants and then combine them, as in the sentences in this
lesson.

Name_____

- Every sentence begins with a capital letter.
- Use the correct end mark for each sentence.
- Use a comma to set off a person's name when the person is spoken to directly.
- Use a comma after introductory words such as *yes*, *no*, and *well*.

Make corrections in this conversation between Sara and her brother Luis, who are visiting an ant farm, by adding correct punctuation and capitalization.

Luis   look at these small carpenter ants Sara

_____

Sara   yes they are small don't they have a lot of wood to eat

_____

Luis   my teacher says that they don't eat the wood they dig it

_____

_____

Sara   they must be very strong look at that big one Luis

_____

Luis   that's the queen ant the ants take special care of her

_____

Sara   what are those little white things Luis

_____

Luis   those are eggs the queen is the only ant that produces them.

_____

_____

Sara   now I understand why she is so special

_____

At Home: Have your child read the above dialogue aloud.
Invite your child to add one or two more lines to it.

The Life and Times of the Ant
Grade 4/Unit 6

187

Name_____

Read the passage below. Combine each pair of underlined sentences into one sentence by adding a prepositional phrase. Write the combination sentences on the lines below.

I read an interesting book. It was about ants. The book says that ants are one of the greatest insects around. Ants protect plants. They protect them from other insects. Also, they feed the dirt with good things so that we can grow pretty flowers, like Mr. Chang's pink roses! There are three kinds of ants that help each other. They help to get things done.

Worker ants look after the other ants. They do this by gathering food, watching the queen and her eggs, and building the anthill. Male ants don't live long, but they help the queen produce lots of eggs. Finally, there's the queen ant. She is the mother of all the ants. Without her, none of the ants would have anything to do! I recommend this book to all kids who want to learn more about ants and the way they live.

1. _____

2. _____

3. _____
   _____

4. _____
   _____
   _____

At Home: Have your child carefully proofread and correct written homework from another subject.

Study the sentences below. Then circle the choice in which the sentences are combined correctly.

1. They saw the ant crawling. It was crawling up an old tree.
   a. They saw a crawling ant up the tree.
   b. They saw a tree ant crawling.
   c. They saw the ant crawling up an old tree.

2. It was carrying a big breadcrumb. The breadcrumb was in its jaws.
   a. It was carrying a big breadcrumb in its jaws.
   b. It was carrying its big jaws.
   c. A big breadcrumb was carrying its jaws.

3. Then the breadcrumb dropped. It dropped to the ground.
   a. Then the ground dropped.
   b. Then the breadcrumb dropped.
   c. Then the breadcrumb dropped to the ground.

4. The ant ran down the tree. It ran into the nest.
   a. The ant ran down the nest.
   b. The ant ran down the tree into the nest.
   c. The nest ran into the ant.

5. Another ant came out. It came from inside the nest.
   a. Another ant was inside the nest.
   b. Another ant came out from another nest.
   c. Another ant came out from inside the nest.

6. Together, they pushed the breadcrumb. They pushed it up the tree.
   a. Together, they pushed the breadcrumb into the tree.
   b. Together, they pushed the breadcrumb up the tree.
   c. They pushed the breadcrumb and the tree together.

Name_____

- Two sentences can be combined by using a **prepositional phrase**.

Mechanics

- Every sentence begins with a capital letter.
- Use the correct end mark for each sentence.
- Use a comma to set off a person's name when the person is spoken to directly.
- Use a comma after introductory words such as *yes*, *no*, and *well*.

Combine the two sentences below to form one sentence. Then add the correct punctuation and capitalization.

1. Kim do you see that ant. It is on top of that anthill

_____

2. yes I see that tiny ant. It is on the anthill

_____

3. it is feeling around cautiously. it is feeling for something

_____

4. hey here comes a hungry lizard. the lizard is coming from behind the tree.

_____

5. the ant disappeared. it went down the anthill

_____

Name

Read each passage and look at the underlined sentences. Is there a better way to write or say each sentence? If there is, which is the better way? Circle your answer.

"Daido," his dad said. (1) "I'll say it more slower, 'Dye-doe.' It means Great Path." That's a good name for a man who had a great adventure, traveling across the Pacific Ocean to a new land. (2) In Chinese, his family name would be given first. And so he was called Wong Daido.

1. **A.** "I'll say it most slower, 'Dye-doe.'
   B. "I'll say it slower, 'Dye-doe.'
   C. "I'll say it slowest, 'Dye-doe.'
   D. No mistake

2. **E.** In Chinese, his family name would be given firstly.
   F. In Chinese, his family name would be first given.
   G. In Chinese, his family name would be given at first.
   H. No mistake

They all laughed. Tucker had a squeaky laugh that sounded as if he were hiccupping. (3) Chester was feeling much happy now. (4) The future did not seem near as gloomy as it had before.

3. **A.** Chester was feeling much happiest now.
   B. Chester was feeling now happier much.
   C. Chester was feeling much happier now.
   D. No mistake

4. **E.** The future did not seem nearly as gloomy as it had before.
   F. The future did not seem near as gloomily as it had before.
   G. The future did not seem nearly as gloomier as it had before.
   H. No mistake

(5) "On a much larger scale," he said, "the machine fails to work good."
They were both puzzled. They did not know this fact. (6) A machine twice as
big needs eight times the power to fly.

5. **A.** "On a much larger scale," he said, "the machine fails to work well."
   B. "On a much larger scale," he said, "the machine fails to work most well."
   C. "On a much larger scale," he said, "the machine fails to work most good."
   D. No mistake

6. **E.** A machine, twice as big, needs eight times the power to fly.
   F. A twice as big machine needs eight times the power to fly.
   G. A twice big machine needs eight big the power to fly.
   H. No mistake

(7) Ants are like humans because they natural need each other to survive.
(8) Worker ants skillfully dig through dirt to build anthills. When they are done,
other worker ants build different rooms to store food and eggs, and trap heat for
warmth.

7. **A.** Ants are like humans because they naturally need each other to
   survive.
   B. Ants are like humans because they more natural need each other to
   survive.
   C. Ants are like humans because they most natural need each other to
   survive.
   D. No mistake

8. **E.** Worker ants skillful dig through dirt to build anthills.
   F. Worker ants skill dig through dirt to build anthills.
   G. Worker ants more skillfully dig through dirt to build anthills.
   H. No mistake